THE GOLDEN HYMN-BOOK

Selected All-time Favorites
To Make the Heart Sing

Compiled by
R. W. STRINGFIELD

Lillenas Publishing Co.
KANSAS CITY, MO. 64141

Contents

Songs for the heart

PERHAPS IT IS NOT STRANGE that, in this day of spectator sports and television, enjoyment of Christian music often begins and ends with merely listening. We should enjoy good Christian music, of course. But what about singing more ourselves? Could it be we are missing something?

Singing is the language of the heart; the Christian who never sings would seem to trudge along in empty silence. And this is not the way that things should be. True, many of us do not have voices which fit us for recruitment by the choir, but—have you ever noticed?—the very resonance of our bodies makes us sound good to ourselves.

It is amazing how quickly singing can change one's inner climate. Try singing when you face a disappointment, when you are boxed into a situation where your temper is about to flare, or when you are depressed. It really works! You'll find you cannot sing for long without a transformation.

For the Christian, singing is like spiritual respiration. By it we breathe in the great realities of Christian truth and send them pulsing to every capillary of the inner man. No wonder we find in Ephesians 5 that the command to be filled with the Spirit is linked with singing. "Be filled with the Spirit," we read, and the next words seem to follow naturally, "speaking to yourselves in psalms and hymns and spiritual songs, singing and making melody in your heart to the Lord."

Notice the emphasis is on singing in the heart. That's where songs are needed most. In fact there are often times when vocalizing is impossible, but that need not interfere with "making melody . . . to the Lord."

What shall we sing? Through the centuries men and women of God have turned to our heritage of hymns. Here they have found all the mighty themes of Christian faith set out with freshness, strength, and beauty. Melodic settings, often familiar, have made them easier to remember.

But still, what shall we sing? Familiar hymns like "Blessed Assurance" and "Saviour, like a Shepherd Lead Us"; great hymns of strength like "A Mighty Fortress Is Our God"; hymns of worship, petition, and rejoicing—and many more. We should make our own selections.

Gospel songs will have a place in the choices of most people, and choruses as well. In the case of hymns, draw on the well-known stanzas first, but then move in to discover and claim the stanzas you have never known. They all are yours.

A treasury of strength and inspiration is at hand in the pages of your hymnal. Real interest is the only key you need. Start reading hymns as poems of the faith. Before you lay the book aside, pick one or two to memorize this week. And then keep on.

But especially keep on singing. For you were born to sing.

Reprinted by permission from April issue of *MOODY MONTHLY*.
Copyright 1975, Moody Bible Institute of Chicago.

1 Blessed Assurance

ASSURANCE

Fanny J. Crosby, 1820 - 1915

Phoebe Palmer Knapp, 1839 - 1908

1. Bless-ed as - sur-ance, Je - sus is mine! Oh, what a fore - taste of
2. Per-fect sub-mis - sion, per-fect de - light! Vi - sions of rap - ture now
3. Per-fect sub-mis - sion, all is at rest. I in my Sav - iour am

glo - ry di - vine! Heir of sal - va - tion, pur-chase of God, Born of His
burst on my sight! An - gels de-scend- ing bring from a - bove Ech - oes of
hap- py and blest; Watching and wait - ing, look-ing a - bove, Filled with His

REFRAIN

Spir - it, washed in His blood!
mer - cy, whis - pers of love. This is my sto - ry, this is my
good-ness, lost in His love.

song, Prais - ing my Sav - iour all the day long. This is my

sto - ry, this is my song, Prais - ing my Sav - iour all the day long.

2 In the Garden

C. Austin Miles, 1868-1946   C. Austin Miles, 1868-1946

1. I come to the gar-den a-lone, While the dew is still on the
2. He speaks, and the sound of His voice Is so sweet the birds hush their
3. I'd stay in the gar-den with Him Tho' the night a-round me be

ros - es; And the voice I hear, Fall-ing on my ear, The
sing - ing, And the mel - o - dy That He gave to me With-
fall - ing, But He bids me go; Thru the voice of woe, His

REFRAIN

Son of God dis - clos - es.
in my heart is ring - ing.   And He walks with me, and He
voice to me is call - ing.

talks with me, And He tells me I am His own; And the

joy we share as we tar - ry there, None oth-er has ev-er known.

3 What a Friend We Have in Jesus

CONVERSE

Joseph M. Scriven, 1820 - 1886

Charles C. Converse, 1832 - 1918

1. What a Friend we have in Je - sus, All our sins and griefs to bear!
2. Have we tri - als and temp - ta - tions? Is there trou - ble an - y - where?
3. Are we weak and heav - y - lad - en, Cum - bered with a load of care?

What a priv - i - lege to car - ry Ev - 'ry-thing to God in pray'r!
We should nev - er be dis - cour-aged; Take it to the Lord in pray'r.
Pre - cious Sav - iour, still our Ref - uge!— Take it to the Lord in pray'r.

Oh, what peace we of - ten for - feit, Oh, what need-less pain we bear,
Can we find a friend so faith - ful Who will all our sor-rows share?
Do thy friends despise, for - sake thee? Take it to the Lord in pray'r.

All be-cause we do not car - ry Ev - 'ry - thing to God in pray'r!
Je - sus knows our ev - 'ry weak-ness; Take it to the Lord in pray'r.
In His arms He'll take and shield thee; Thou wilt find a sol - ace there.

4
Rock of Ages

TOPLADY

Augustus M. Toplady, 1740-1778

Thomas Hastings, 1784-1872

1. Rock of A - ges, cleft for me, Let me hide my - self in Thee.
2. Could my tears for - ev - er flow, Could my zeal no lan - guor know,
3. While I draw this fleet - ing breath, When my eyes shall close in death,

Let the wa - ter and the blood, From Thy wound-ed side which flowed,
These for sin could not a - tone; Thou must save, and Thou a - lone.
When I rise to worlds un-known, And be - hold Thee on Thy throne,

Be of sin the dou - ble cure, Save from wrath and make me pure.
In my hand no price I bring; Sim - ply to Thy cross I cling.
Rock of A - ges, cleft for me, Let me hide my - self in Thee.

5
Amazing Grace

John Newton, 1725-1807

Early American Melody

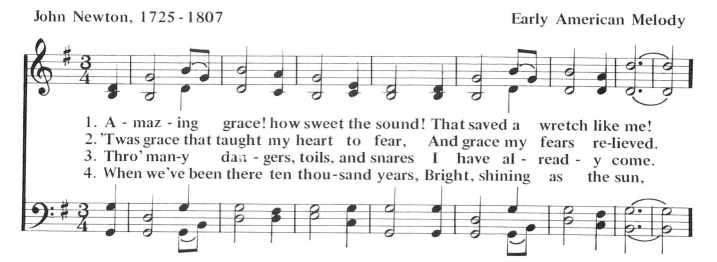

1. A - maz - ing grace! how sweet the sound! That saved a wretch like me!
2. 'Twas grace that taught my heart to fear, And grace my fears re-lieved.
3. Thro' man-y dan - gers, toils, and snares I have al - read - y come.
4. When we've been there ten thou-sand years, Bright, shining as the sun,

I once was lost, but now am found; Was blind, but now I see.
How pre - cious did that grace ap - pear The hour I first be-lieved!
'Tis grace hath bro't me safe thus far, And grace will lead me home.
We've no less days to sing God's praise Than when we first be - gun.

6   Abide with Me

EVENTIDE

Henry F. Lyte, 1793 - 1847   William H. Monk, 1823 - 1889

1. A - bide with me! Fast falls the e - ven - tide. The dark-ness
2. Swift to its close ebbs out life's lit - tle day. Earth's joys grow
3. I need Thy pres - ence ev - 'ry pass-ing hour. What but Thy
4. I fear no foe, with Thee at hand to bless; Ills have no
5. Hold Thou Thy cross be - fore my clos - ing eyes; Shine thro' the

deep - ens; Lord, with me a - bide! When oth - er help - ers
dim; its glo - ries pass a - way. Change and de - cay in
grace can foil the tempt-er's pow'r? Who, like thy - self, my
weight, and tears no bit - ter - ness. Where is death's sting? Where,
gloom, and point me to the skies. Heav'n's morning breaks, and

fail and com-forts flee, Help of the help - less, oh, a - bide with me!
all a - round I see; O Thou who changest not, a - bide with me!
guide and stay can be? Thro' cloud and sun-shine, oh, a - bide with me!
grave, thy vic - to - ry? I tri-umph still if Thou a - bide with me.
earth's vain shad-ows flee! In life, in death, O Lord, a - bide with me!

7 Love Divine, All Loves Excelling

BEECHER

Charles Wesley, 1707-1788

John Zundel, 1815-1882

1. Love di - vine, all loves ex -cel-ling, Joy of heav'n, to earth come down!
2. Breathe,oh,breathe Thy lov - ing Spir - it In - to ev - 'ry trou-bled breast!
3. Come, Al-might - y to De - liv - er; Let us all Thy life re - ceive.
4. Fin - ish then Thy new cre - a - tion; Pure and spot - less let us be.

Fix in us Thy hum-ble dwell-ing; All Thy faith - ful mer - cies crown.
Let us all in Thee in - her - it; Let us find that sec - ond rest.
Sud - den -ly re - turn, and nev - er, Nev - er -more Thy tem - ples leave.
Let us see Thy great sal - va - tion, Per - fect - ly re - stored in Thee:

Je - sus, Thou art all com - pas - sion; Pure, un-bound-ed love Thou art.
Take a - way our bent to sin - ning; Al - pha and O - me - ga be.
Thee we would be al - ways bless - ing, Serve Thee as Thy hosts a - bove,
Changed from glo - ry in - to glo - ry, Till in heav'n we take our place,

Vis - it us with Thy sal - va - tion; En - ter ev - 'ry trem-bling heart.
End of faith, as its Be - gin - ning, Set our hearts at lib - er - ty.
Pray, and praise Thee with - out ceas - ing, Glo - ry in Thy per - fect love.
Till we cast our crowns be - fore Thee, Lost in won - der, love, and praise.

8

Come, Thou Fount
NETTLETON

Robert Robinson, 1735-1790
3rd Stanza Alt. 1931

John Wyeth, 1770-1858

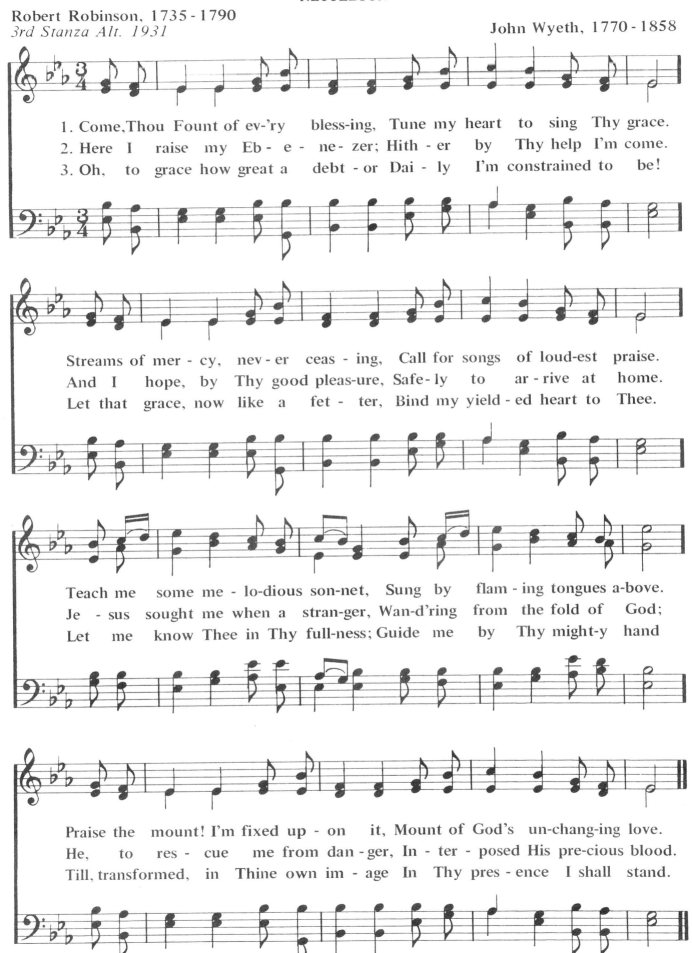

1. Come, Thou Fount of ev-'ry bless-ing, Tune my heart to sing Thy grace.
2. Here I raise my Eb-e-ne-zer; Hith-er by Thy help I'm come.
3. Oh, to grace how great a debt-or Dai-ly I'm constrained to be!

Streams of mer-cy, nev-er ceas-ing, Call for songs of loud-est praise.
And I hope, by Thy good pleas-ure, Safe-ly to ar-rive at home.
Let that grace, now like a fet-ter, Bind my yield-ed heart to Thee.

Teach me some me-lo-dious son-net, Sung by flam-ing tongues a-bove.
Je-sus sought me when a stran-ger, Wan-d'ring from the fold of God;
Let me know Thee in Thy full-ness; Guide me by Thy might-y hand

Praise the mount! I'm fixed up-on it, Mount of God's un-chang-ing love.
He, to res-cue me from dan-ger, In-ter-posed His pre-cious blood.
Till, transformed, in Thine own im-age In Thy pres-ence I shall stand.

9 Fairest Lord Jesus

CRUSADERS' HYMN

From the German, 17th Century

From "Schlesische Volkslieder"
Arr. by Richard S. Willis, 1819-1900

1. Fair - est Lord Je - sus! Rul - er of all na - ture!
2. Fair are the mead - ows; Fair - er still the wood - lands,
3. Fair is the sun - shine, Fair - er still the moon - light,
4. Beau - ti - ful Sav - iour! Lord of all the na - tions!

O Thou of God and man the Son! Thee will I cher - ish,
Robed in the bloom - ing garb of spring. Je - sus is fair - er,
And all the twin - kling star - ry host. Je - sus shines bright - er,
The Son of God and Son of Man! Glo - ry and hon - or,

Thee will I hon - or, Thou, my soul's glo - ry, joy, and crown!
Je - sus is pur - er, Who makes the woe - ful heart to sing!
Je - sus shines pur - er, Than all the an - gels heav'n can boast!
Praise, ad - o - ra - tion, Now and for - ev - er - more be Thine!

10 Jesus, the Very Thought of Thee

ST. AGNES

Bernard of Clairvaux, 12th Century
Trans. by Edward Caswall, 1814-1878

John B. Dykes, 1823-1876

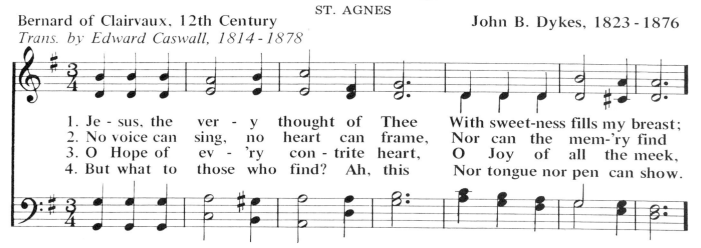

1. Je - sus, the ver - y thought of Thee With sweet-ness fills my breast;
2. No voice can sing, no heart can frame, Nor can the mem-'ry find
3. O Hope of ev - 'ry con - trite heart, O Joy of all the meek,
4. But what to those who find? Ah, this Nor tongue nor pen can show.

But sweeter far Thy face to see, And in Thy pres-ence rest.
A sweet-er sound than Thy blest name, O Sav-iour of man-kind!
To those who fall, how kind Thou art! How good to those who seek!
The love of Je - sus, what it is None but His loved ones know.

11   Saviour, More than Life
EVERY DAY AND HOUR

Fanny J. Crosby, 1820 - 1915   William H. Doane, 1832 - 1915

1. Sav-iour, more than life to me, I am cling-ing, cling-ing close to Thee.
2. Thro' this chang-ing world be - low Lead me gent-ly, gent-ly as I go.
3. Let me love Thee more and more Till this fleet-ing, fleet-ing life is o'er;

Let Thy pre-cious blood ap - plied Keep me ev - er, ev - er near Thy side.
Trusting Thee, I can - not stray; I can nev-er, nev - er lose my way.
Till my soul is lost in love In a bright-er, bright-er world a - bove.

REFRAIN

Ev - 'ry day, ev - 'ry hour, Let me feel Thy cleansing pow'r.
Ev - 'ry day and hour, ev - 'ry day and hour,

May Thy ten - der love to me Bind me clos - er, clos- er, Lord, to Thee.

12 Come, Thou Almighty King

ITALIAN HYMN (Trinity)

Anonymous

Felice de Giardini, 1716 - 1796

1. Come, Thou Al-might-y King. Help us Thy name to sing.
2. Come, Thou In-car-nate Word, Gird on Thy might-y sword,
3. Come, Ho-ly Com-fort-er, Thy sa-cred wit-ness bear
4. To the great One in Three E-ter-nal prais-es be

Help us to praise. Fa-ther, all-glo-ri-ous, O'er all vic-
Our prayer at-tend. Come, and Thy peo-ple bless, And give Thy
In this glad hour. Thou who al-might-y art, Now rule in
Hence ev-er-more. His sov-'reign maj-es-ty May we in

to-ri-ous, Come and reign o-ver us, An-cient of Days.
Word suc-cess. Spir-it of ho-li-ness, On us de-scend.
ev-'ry heart; And ne'er from us de-part, Spir-it of pow'r.
glo-ry see, And to e-ter-ni-ty Love and a-dore.

13 Praise God, from Whom All Blessings Flow

DOXOLOGY

Thomas Ken, 1637 - 1711

Louis Bourgeois, 1510 - 1561

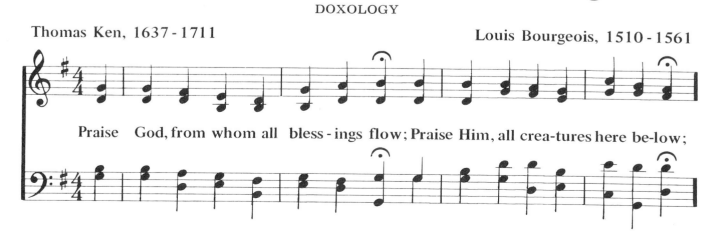

Praise God, from whom all bless-ings flow; Praise Him, all crea-tures here be-low;

Praise Him a-bove, ye heav'n-ly host. Praise Fa-ther, Son, and Ho-ly Ghost.

14   I Need Thee Every Hour

NEED

Annie S. Hawks, 1835-1918   Robert Lowry, 1826-1899

1. I need Thee ev-'ry hour, Most gra-cious Lord; No ten-der voice like
2. I need Thee ev-'ry hour; Stay Thou near - by. Temp-ta-tions lose their
3. I need Thee ev-'ry hour, In joy or pain; Come quick-ly and a-
4. I need Thee ev-'ry hour, Most Ho - ly One. Oh, make me Thine in-

REFRAIN

Thine Can peace af - ford.
pow'r When Thou art nigh.   I need Thee; oh, I need Thee! Ev-'ry hour I
bide, Or life is vain.
deed, Thou bless - ed Son!

need Thee! Oh, bless me now, my Sav-iour; I come to Thee!

15   O Worship the King

LYONS

Robert Grant, 1785-1838   Johann Michael Haydn, 1737-1806

1. O wor-ship the King, all glo-rious a-bove, And grate-ful-ly
2. O tell of His might, and sing of His grace, Whose robe is the
3. Thy boun-ti-ful care, what tongue can re-cite? It breathes in the
4. Frail chil-dren of dust, and fee-ble as frail, In Thee do we

sing His won-der-ful love: Our Shield and De-fend-er, the
light, whose can-o-py space. His char-iots of wrath the deep
air; it shines in the light. It streams from the hills; it de-
trust, nor find Thee to fail. Thy mer-cies how ten-der! how

An-cient of Days, Pa-vil-ioned in splen-dor, and gird-ed with praise.
thun-der-clouds form, And dark is His path on the wings of the storm.
scends to the plain, And sweet-ly dis-tills in the dew and the rain.
firm to the end! Our Mak-er, De-fend-er, Re-deem-er, and Friend!

16   Majestic Sweetness

ORTONVILLE

Samuel Stennett, 1727-1795   Thomas Hastings, 1784-1872

1. Ma-jes-tic sweetness sits enthroned Up-on the Saviour's brow; His head with
2. No mor-tal can with Him compare A-mong the sons of men; Fair-er is
3. He saw me plunged in deep dis-tress, And flew to my re-lief; For me He
4. To Him I owe my life and breath And all the joys I have; He makes me
5. Since from His boun-ty I re-ceive Such proofs of love di-vine, Had I a

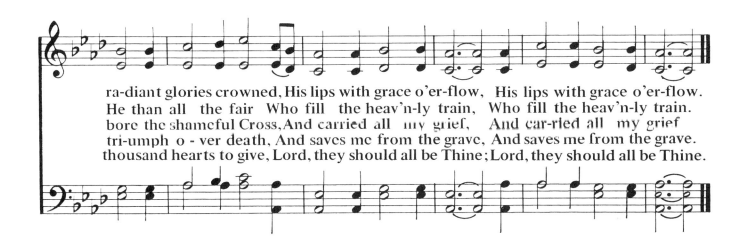

ra-diant glories crowned, His lips with grace o'er-flow, His lips with grace o'er-flow.
He than all the fair Who fill the heav'n-ly train, Who fill the heav'n-ly train.
bore the shameful Cross, And carried all my grief, And car-ried all my grief
tri-umph o - ver death, And saves me from the grave, And saves me from the grave.
thousand hearts to give, Lord, they should all be Thine; Lord, they should all be Thine.

17 Holy, Holy, Holy, Lord God Almighty

NICAEA

Reginald Heber, 1783 - 1826   John B. Dykes, 1823 - 1876

1. Ho-ly, Ho-ly, Ho - ly, Lord God Al - might - y! Ear - ly in the
2. Ho-ly, Ho-ly. Ho - ly! All the saints a - dore Thee, Casting down their
3. Ho-ly, Ho-ly, Ho - ly! Tho' the darkness hide Thee, Tho' the eye of
4. Ho-ly, Ho-ly, Ho - ly! Lord God Al - might - y! All Thy works shall

morn - ing our song shall rise to Thee. Ho-ly, Ho - ly, Ho - ly!
gold - en crowns a - round the glass - y sea; Cher - u - bim and ser-a-phim
sin - ful man Thy glo - ry may not see, On - ly Thou art ho - ly;
praise Thy name in earth, and sky, and sea. Ho-ly, Ho - ly, Ho - ly!

Mer - ci - ful and Might - y! God in three Per - sons, bless-ed Trin - i - ty!
fall - ing down be-fore Thee, Which wert, and art, and ev - er-more shalt be.
there is none be-side Thee Per - fect in pow'r, in love, in pu - ri - ty.
Mer - ci - ful and Might - y! God in three Per - sons, bless-ed Trin - i - ty!

18 The Church's One Foundation

AURELIA

Samuel J. Stone, 1839-1900

Samuel S. Wesley, 1810-1876

1. The Church's one Foun-da-tion Is Je-sus Christ, her Lord.
2. E-lect from ev-'ry na-tion, Yet one o'er all the earth;
3. 'Mid toil and trib-u-la-tion, And tu-mult of her war,
4. Yet she on earth hath u-nion With God, the Three in One,

She is His new cre-a-tion By wa-ter and the word.
Her char-ter of sal-va-tion, One Lord, one faith, one birth;
She waits the con-sum-ma-tion Of peace for-ev-er-more;
And mys-tic, sweet com-mu-nion With those whose rest is won.

From heav'n He came and sought her To be His ho-ly bride; With
One ho-ly name she bless-es; Par-takes one ho-ly food; And
Till, with the vi-sion glo-rious, Her long-ing eyes are blest, And
Oh, hap-py ones and ho-ly! Lord, give us grace that we, Like

His own blood He bought her, And for her life He died.
to one hope she press-es, With ev-'ry grace en-dued.
the great Church vic-to-rious Shall be the Church at rest.
them, the meek and low-ly, On high may dwell with Thee.

19   To God Be the Glory

Fanny J. Crosby, 1820 - 1915

W. H. Doane, 1832 - 1915

1. To God be the glory—great things He hath done. So loved He the world that He
2. O per - fect re-demp-tion, the purchase of blood, To ev - 'ry be - liev - er the
3. Great things He hath taught us, great things He hath done, And great our rejoicing thro'

gave us His Son, Who yielded His life an a - tone-ment for sin, And opened the
prom-ise of God! The vil - est of - fend-er who tru - ly believes, That moment from
Je - sus, the Son; But pu - rer, and higher, and greater will be Our won-der, our

REFRAIN

Life - gate that all may go in.
Je - sus a par-don receives. Praise the Lord, praise the Lord, Let the earth hear His
transport, when Je-sus we see.

voice! Praise the Lord, praise the Lord, Let the peo-ple re - joice! O come to the

Fa-ther, thro' Je-sus, the Son, And give Him the glo-ry—great things He hath done.

20 Onward, Christian Soldiers

ST. GERTRUDE

Sabine Baring-Gould, 1834-1924

Arthur Sullivan, 1842-1900

1. On-ward, Christian sol-diers! March-ing as to war, With the cross of Je-sus Go-ing on be-fore. Christ, the roy-al Mas-ter, Leads a-gainst the foe; For-ward in-to bat-tle, See, His ban-ners go!
2. Like a might-y ar-my Moves the Church of God. Broth-ers, we are tread-ing Where the saints have trod. We are not di-vid-ed; All one bod-y we: One in hope and doc-trine, One in char-i-ty.
3. Crowns and thrones may per-ish, King-doms rise and wane; But the Church of Je-sus Con-stant will re-main. Gates of hell can nev-er 'Gainst that Church prevail; We have Christ's own promise, Which can nev-er fail.
4. On-ward, then, ye peo-ple! Join our hap-py throng; Blend with ours your voic-es In the tri-umph song. Glo-ry, laud, and hon-or Un-to Christ, the King; This thro' count-less a-ges Men and an-gels sing.

REFRAIN

On-ward, Chris-tian sol-diers! March-ing as to war, With the cross of Je-sus Go-ing on be-fore.

21

O God, Our Help in Ages Past

ST. ANNE

Isaac Watts, 1674 - 1748

William Croft, 1678 - 1727

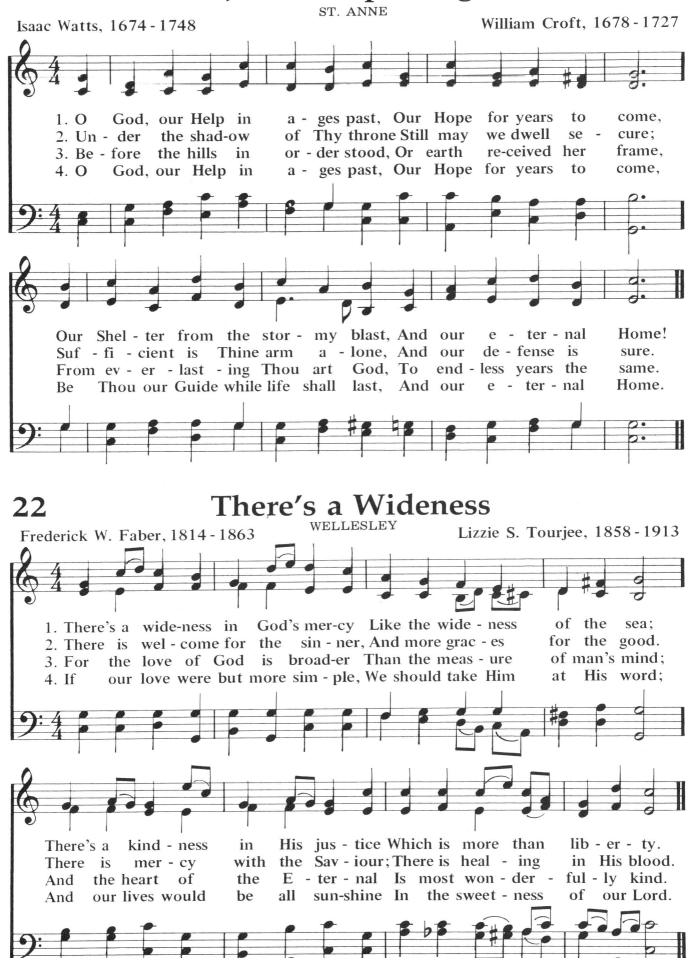

1. O God, our Help in a - ges past, Our Hope for years to come,
2. Un - der the shad-ow of Thy throne Still may we dwell se - cure;
3. Be - fore the hills in or - der stood, Or earth re-ceived her frame,
4. O God, our Help in a - ges past, Our Hope for years to come,

Our Shel - ter from the stor - my blast, And our e - ter - nal Home!
Suf - fi - cient is Thine arm a - lone, And our de - fense is sure.
From ev - er - last - ing Thou art God, To end - less years the same.
Be Thou our Guide while life shall last, And our e - ter - nal Home.

22

There's a Wideness

WELLESLEY

Frederick W. Faber, 1814 - 1863

Lizzie S. Tourjee, 1858 - 1913

1. There's a wide-ness in God's mer-cy Like the wide - ness of the sea;
2. There is wel - come for the sin - ner, And more grac - es for the good.
3. For the love of God is broad-er Than the meas - ure of man's mind;
4. If our love were but more sim - ple, We should take Him at His word;

There's a kind - ness in His jus - tice Which is more than lib - er - ty.
There is mer - cy with the Sav - iour; There is heal - ing in His blood.
And the heart of the E - ter - nal Is most won - der - ful - ly kind.
And our lives would be all sun-shine In the sweet - ness of our Lord.

23 A Mighty Fortress Is Our God

EIN FESTE BURG

Martin Luther, 1483-1546
Tr. by Frederick H. Hedge, 1805-1890

Martin Luther, 1483-1546

1. A might-y For-tress is our God, A Bul-wark nev-er fail - ing;
2. Did we in our own strength con-fide, Our striv-ing would be los - ing,
3. And though this world, with devils filled, Should threaten to un-do us,
4. That word a-bove all earth - ly powers, No thanks to them, a - bid - eth;

Our Help-er He, a - mid the flood Of mor-tal ills pre-vail - ing.
Were not the right Man on our side, The Man of God's own choos - ing.
We will not fear, for God hath willed His truth to tri - umph through us.
The Spir-it and the gifts are ours Through Him who with us sid - eth.

For still our an - cient foe Doth seek to work us woe; His craft and power are
Dost ask who that may be? Christ Je - sus, it is He; Lord Sa - ba - oth, His
The prince of dark-ness grim— We trem-ble not for him. His rage we can en-
Let goods and kin-dred go, This mor - tal life al - so. The bod - y they may

great, And, armed with cru - el hate, On earth is not his e - qual.
name, From age to age the same, And He must win the bat - tle.
dure, For, lo, his doom is sure; One lit - tle word shall fell him.
kill; God's truth a - bid - eth still. His king-dom is for - ev - er.

24 How Firm a Foundation

FOUNDATION

"K" in Rippon's "A Selection of Hymns," 1787   Early American Melody

1. How firm a foun - da - tion, ye saints of the Lord,
2. Fear not; I am with thee. Oh, be not dis - mayed,
3. When thro' the deep wa - ters I call thee to go,
4. When thro' fie - ry tri - als thy path - way shall lie,
5. E'en down to old age all My peo - ple shall prove
6. The soul that on Je - sus hath leaned for re - pose

Is laid for your faith in His ex - cel - lent Word!
For I am thy God, I will still give thee aid.
The riv - ers of sor - row shall not o - ver - flow;
My grace, all - suf - fi - cient, shall be thy sup - ply.
My sov' - reign, e - ter - nal, un - change - a - ble love;
I will not, I will not de - sert to his foes;

What more can He say than to you He hath said,
I'll strength - en thee, help thee, and cause thee to stand,
For I will be with thee thy tri - als to bless,
The flames shall not hurt thee; I on - ly de - sign
And when hoar - y hairs shall their tem - ples a - dorn,
That soul, tho' all hell should en - deav - or to shake,

To you who for ref - uge to Je - sus have fled?
Up - held by My gra - cious, om - nip - o - tent hand.
And sanc - ti - fy to thee thy deep - est dis - tress.
Thy dross to con - sume and thy gold to re - fine.
Like lambs they shall still in My bos - om be borne.
I'll nev - er, no nev - er, no nev - er for - sake.

25 Take My Life, and Let It Be

HENDON

Frances R. Havergal, 1836 - 1879

Henri A. Cesar Malan, 1787 - 1864

1. Take my life, and let it be Con-se-crat-ed, Lord, to
2. Take my feet, and let them be Swift and beau-ti-ful for
3. Take my lips, and let them be Filled with mes-sag-es for
4. Take my will and make it Thine; It shall be no lon-ger
5. Take my love; my God, I pour At Thy feet its treas-ure

Thee. Take my hands, and let them move At the
Thee. Take my voice, and let me sing Al-ways,
Thee. Take my sil-ver and my gold; Not a
mine. Take my heart; it is Thine own! It shall
store. Take my-self and I will be Ev-er,

im-pulse of Thy love, At the im-pulse of Thy love.
on-ly, for my King; Al-ways, on-ly, for my King.
mite would I with-hold, Not a mite would I with-hold.
be Thy roy-al throne. It shall be Thy roy-al throne.
on-ly, all for Thee; Ev-er, on-ly, all for Thee.

26 When Morning Gilds the Skies

LAUDES DOMINI

From the German, 19th Century
Trans. by Edward Caswall, 1814 - 1878

Joseph Barnby, 1838 - 1896

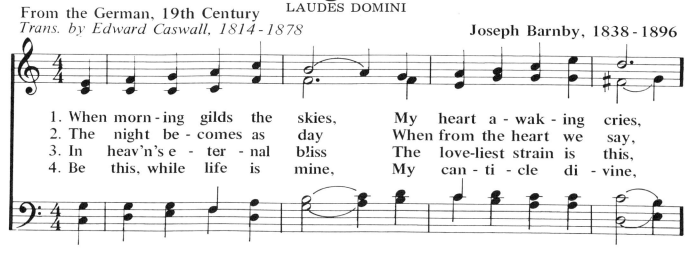

1. When morn-ing gilds the skies, My heart a-wak-ing cries,
2. The night be-comes as day When from the heart we say,
3. In heav'n's e-ter-nal bliss The love-liest strain is this,
4. Be this, while life is mine, My can-ti-cle di-vine,

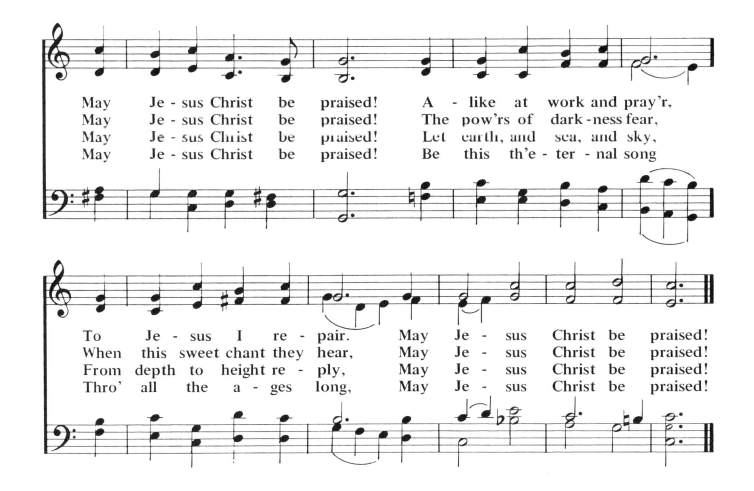

May Je-sus Christ be praised! A - like at work and pray'r,
May Je-sus Christ be praised! The pow'rs of dark-ness fear,
May Je-sus Christ be praised! Let earth, and sea, and sky,
May Je-sus Christ be praised! Be this th'e-ter-nal song

To Je-sus I re-pair. May Je-sus Christ be praised!
When this sweet chant they hear, May Je-sus Christ be praised!
From depth to height re-ply, May Je-sus Christ be praised!
Thro' all the a-ges long, May Je-sus Christ be praised!

27   Dear Lord and Father of Mankind

REST

John Greenleaf Whittier, 1807 - 1892   Frederick C. Maker, 1844 - 1927

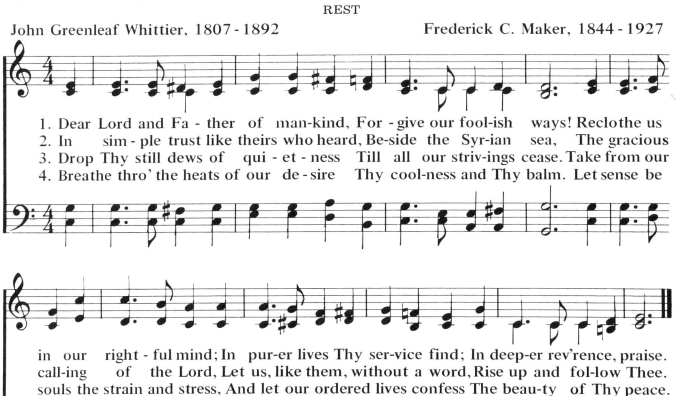

1. Dear Lord and Fa - ther of man-kind, For - give our fool-ish ways! Reclothe us
2. In sim - ple trust like theirs who heard, Be-side the Syr-ian sea, The gracious
3. Drop Thy still dews of qui - et - ness Till all our striv-ings cease. Take from our
4. Breathe thro' the heats of our de - sire Thy cool-ness and Thy balm. Let sense be

in our right - ful mind; In pur-er lives Thy ser-vice find; In deep-er rev'rence, praise.
call-ing of the Lord, Let us, like them, without a word, Rise up and fol-low Thee.
souls the strain and stress, And let our ordered lives confess The beau-ty of Thy peace.
dumb, let flesh retire; Speak thro' the earthquake, wind, and fire, O still small voice of calm!

28 Wonderful Peace

W. D. Cornell, Alt.,19th Century

W. G. Cooper, 19th Century

1. Far a-way in the depths of my spir-it to-night Rolls a
2. What a treas-ure I have in this won-der-ful peace, Bur-ied
3. I am rest-ing to-night in this won-der-ful peace, Rest-ing
4. And me-thinks when I rise to that cit-y of peace, Where the
5. Ah! soul, are you here with-out com-fort or rest, March-ing

mel-o-dy sweet-er than psalm; In ce-les-tial-like strains it un-
deep in the heart of my soul, So se-cure that no pow-er can
sweet-ly in Je-sus' con-trol; For I'm kept from all dan-ger by
Au-thor of peace I shall see, That one strain of the song which the
down the rough path-way of time? Make Je-sus your Friend ere the

ceas-ing-ly falls O'er my soul like an in-fi-nite calm.
mine it a-way While the years of e-ter-ni-ty roll!
night and by day, And His glo-ry is flood-ing my soul.
ran-somed will sing In that heav-en-ly King-dom shall be:
shad-ows grow dark. Oh, ac-cept this sweet peace so sub-lime!

REFRAIN

Peace! peace! won-der-ful peace, Coming down from the Fa-ther a-bove! Sweep

o-ver my spir-it for-ev-er, I pray, In fath-om-less bil-lows of love.

29   It Is Well with My Soul

VILLE DE HAVRE

Horatio G. Spafford, 1828 - 1888   Philip P. Bliss, 1838 - 1876

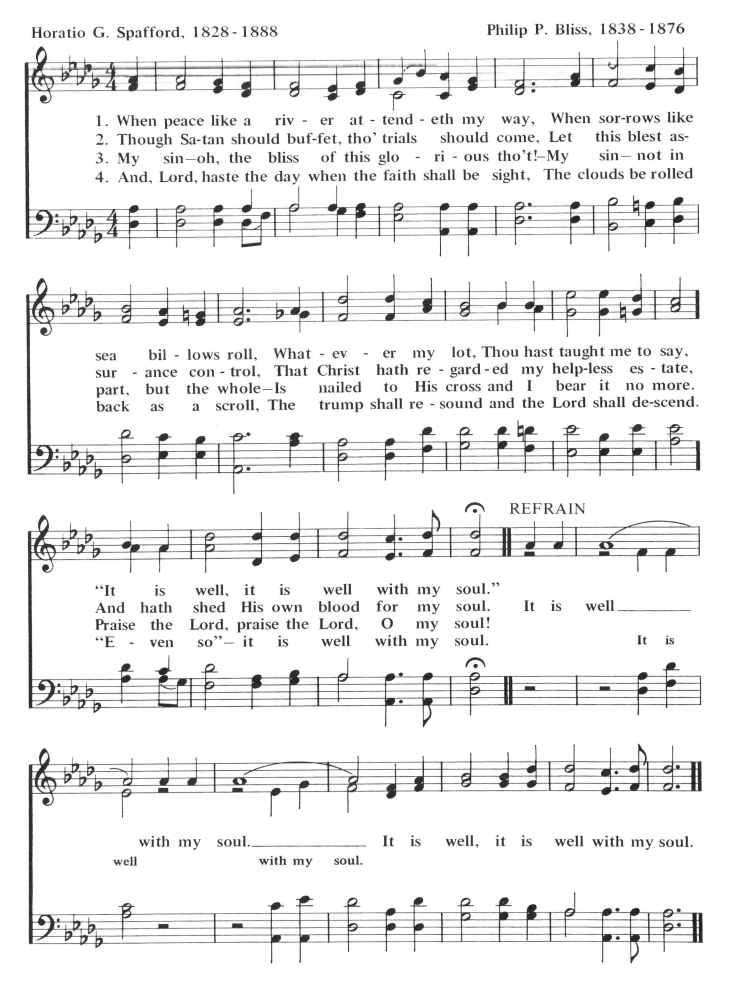

1. When peace like a riv-er at-tend-eth my way, When sor-rows like
2. Though Sa-tan should buf-fet, tho' trials should come, Let this blest as-
3. My sin—oh, the bliss of this glo-ri-ous tho't!—My sin— not in
4. And, Lord, haste the day when the faith shall be sight, The clouds be rolled

sea bil-lows roll, What-ev-er my lot, Thou hast taught me to say,
sur-ance con-trol, That Christ hath re-gard-ed my help-less es-tate,
part, but the whole—Is nailed to His cross and I bear it no more.
back as a scroll, The trump shall re-sound and the Lord shall de-scend.

REFRAIN

"It is well, it is well with my soul."
And hath shed His own blood for my soul. It is well_____
Praise the Lord, praise the Lord, O my soul!
"E-ven so"— it is well with my soul. It is

with my soul._____ It is well, it is well with my soul.
well   with my soul.

30   For the Beauty of the Earth

DIX

Folliott S. Pierpoint, 1835 - 1917   Conrad Kocher, 1786 - 1872

1. For the beau - ty of the earth, For the glo - ry of the skies,
2. For the won - der of each hour Of the day and of the night,
3. For the joy of hu - man love, Broth-er, sis - ter, par-ent, child;
4. For Thy Church that ev - er - more Lift-eth ho - ly hands a - bove,

For the love which from our birth O - ver and a - round us lies,
Hill and vale, and tree and flower, Sun and moon, and stars of light,
Friends on earth, and friends a - bove; For all gen - tle thoughts and mild;
Of - fering up on ev - 'ry shore Her pure sac - ri - fice of love,

Lord of all, to Thee we raise This our hymn of grate - ful praise.

31   Sun of My Soul

HURSLEY

John Keble, 1792 - 1866   *Adapt. from* "Katholisches Gesangbuch," Vienna, 1774

1. Sun of my soul! Thou Sav - iour dear, It is not night if Thou be near.
2. When the soft dews of kind - ly sleep My wea-ry eye - lids gent - ly steep,
3. A-bide with me from morn till eve, For with-out Thee I can - not live.
4. Be near to bless me when I wake, Ere thro' the world my way I take.

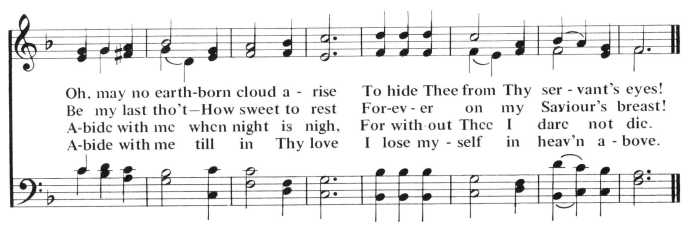

Oh, may no earth-born cloud a - rise   To hide Thee from Thy ser - vant's eyes!
Be my last tho't—How sweet to rest   For-ev - er on my Saviour's breast!
A-bide with me when night is nigh,   For with-out Thee I dare not die.
A-bide with me till in Thy love   I lose my - self in heav'n a - bove.

32 More Love to Thee

Elizabeth Prentiss, 1818 - 1878   William H. Doane, 1832 - 1915

1. More love to Thee, O Christ, More love to Thee! Hear Thou the
2. Once earth - ly joy I craved, Sought peace and rest. Now Thee a-
3. Then shall my lat - est breath Whis - per Thy praise. This be the

prayer I make On bend-ed knee. This is my ear - nest plea:
lone I seek; Give what is best. This all my prayer shall be:
part - ing cry My heart shall raise; This still my prayer shall be:

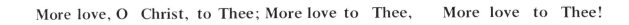

More love, O Christ, to Thee; More love to Thee,   More love to Thee!

33 O Jesus, I Have Promised

ANGEL'S STORY

John E. Bode, 1816 - 1874

Arthur H. Mann, 1850 - 1929

1. O Je - sus, I have prom - ised To serve Thee to the end;
2. O let me feel Thee near me! The world is ev - er near.
3. O Je - sus, Thou hast prom - ised To all who fol - low Thee

Be Thou for - ev - er near me, My Mas - ter and my Friend.
I see the sights that daz - zle; The tempt - ing sounds I hear.
That where Thou art in glo - ry There shall Thy ser - vant be.

I shall not fear the bat - tle If Thou art by my side,
My foes are ev - er near me, A - round me and with - in;
And, Je - sus, I have prom - ised To serve Thee to the end.

Nor wan - der from the path - way If Thou wilt be my Guide.
But, Je - sus, draw Thou near - er, And shield my soul from sin.
O give me grace to fol - low, My Mas - ter and my Friend.

34 This Is My Father's World

TERRA BEATA

Maltbie D. Babcock, 1858-1901

Franklin L. Sheppard, 1852-1930

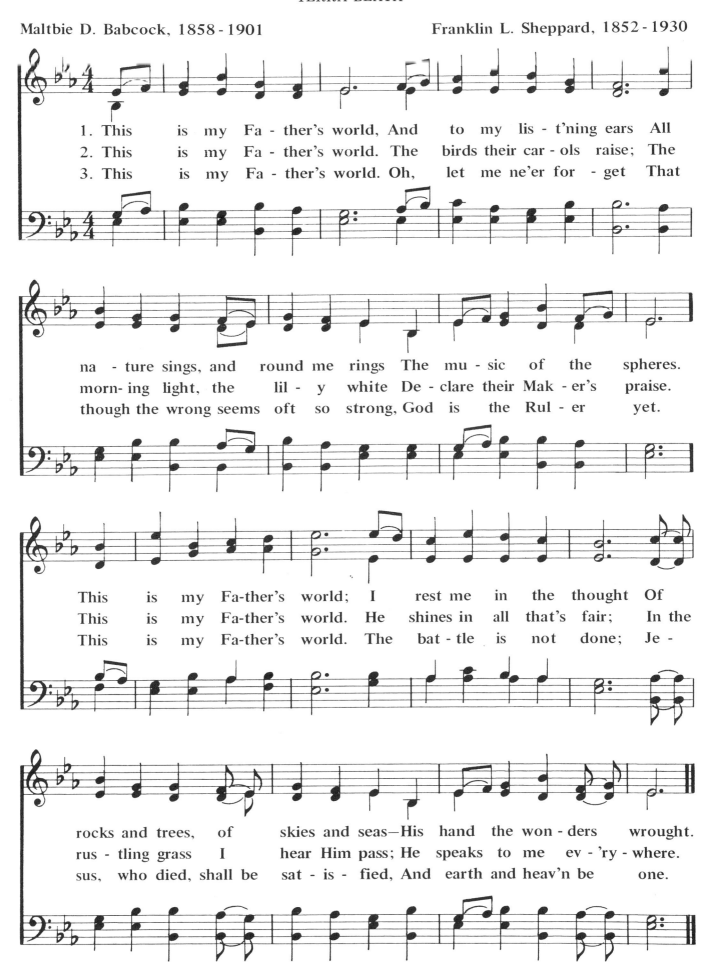

1. This is my Fa-ther's world, And to my lis-t'ning ears All
2. This is my Fa-ther's world. The birds their car-ols raise; The
3. This is my Fa-ther's world. Oh, let me ne'er for-get That

na - ture sings, and round me rings The mu-sic of the spheres.
morn-ing light, the lil - y white De-clare their Mak-er's praise.
though the wrong seems oft so strong, God is the Rul-er yet.

This is my Fa-ther's world; I rest me in the thought Of
This is my Fa-ther's world. He shines in all that's fair; In the
This is my Fa-ther's world. The bat-tle is not done; Je -

rocks and trees, of skies and seas—His hand the won-ders wrought.
rus - tling grass I hear Him pass; He speaks to me ev-'ry-where.
sus, who died, shall be sat - is - fied, And earth and heav'n be one.

35 All Hail the Power of Jesus' Name

CORONATION

Edward Perronet, 1726-1792
Alt. by John Rippon, 1751-1836

Oliver Holden, 1765-1844

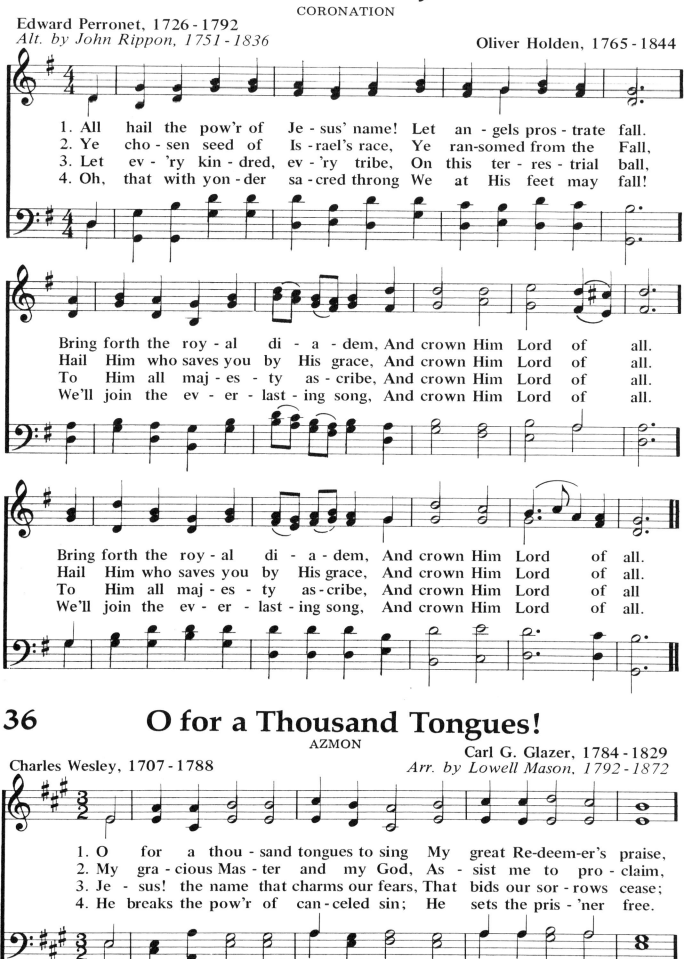

1. All hail the pow'r of Je-sus' name! Let an-gels pros-trate fall.
2. Ye cho-sen seed of Is-rael's race, Ye ran-somed from the Fall,
3. Let ev-'ry kin-dred, ev-'ry tribe, On this ter-res-trial ball,
4. Oh, that with yon-der sa-cred throng We at His feet may fall!

Bring forth the roy-al di-a-dem, And crown Him Lord of all.
Hail Him who saves you by His grace, And crown Him Lord of all.
To Him all maj-es-ty as-cribe, And crown Him Lord of all.
We'll join the ev-er-last-ing song, And crown Him Lord of all.

Bring forth the roy-al di-a-dem, And crown Him Lord of all.
Hail Him who saves you by His grace, And crown Him Lord of all.
To Him all maj-es-ty as-cribe, And crown Him Lord of all
We'll join the ev-er-last-ing song, And crown Him Lord of all.

36 O for a Thousand Tongues!

AZMON

Charles Wesley, 1707-1788

Carl G. Glazer, 1784-1829
Arr. by Lowell Mason, 1792-1872

1. O for a thou-sand tongues to sing My great Re-deem-er's praise,
2. My gra-cious Mas-ter and my God, As-sist me to pro-claim,
3. Je-sus! the name that charms our fears, That bids our sor-rows cease;
4. He breaks the pow'r of can-celed sin; He sets the pris-'ner free.

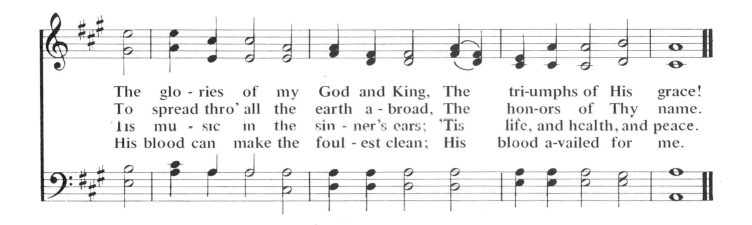

The glo-ries of my God and King, The tri-umphs of His grace!
To spread thro' all the earth a-broad, The hon-ors of Thy name.
'Tis mu-sic in the sin-ner's ears; 'Tis life, and health, and peace.
His blood can make the foul-est clean; His blood a-vailed for me.

37   O Thou in Whose Presence

DAVIS (MEDITATION)

Joseph Swain, 1761 - 1796   Freeman Lewis, 1780 - 1859

1. O Thou in whose pres - ence my soul takes de - light, On
2. Where dost Thou, dear Shep - herd, re - sort with Thy sheep, To
3. Oh, why should I wan - der, an al - ien from Thee, Or
4. He looks! and ten thou - sands of an - gels re - joice, And
5. Dear Shep - herd! I hear and will fol - low Thy call; I

whom in af - flic - tion I call, My Com - fort by day and my
feed them in pas - tures of love? Say, why in the val - ley of
cry in the des - ert for bread? Thy foes will re - joice when my
myr - i - ads wait for His word. He speaks! and e - ter - ni - ty,
know the sweet sound of Thy voice. Re - store and de - fend me, for

Song in the night, My Hope, my Sal - va - tion, my All!
death should I weep, Or a - lone in this wil - der - ness rove?
sor - rows they see, And smile at the tears I have shed.
filled with His voice, Re - ech - oes the praise of the Lord.
Thou art my all, And in Thee I will ev - er re - joice.

38 I Will Praise Him

Margaret J. Harris, 19th Century   Margaret J. Harris, 19th Century

1. When I saw the cleansing foun - tain O - pen wide for all my sin,
2. Tho' the way seem'd straight and narrow, All I claimed was swept a - way;
3. Then God's fire up-on the al - tar Of my heart was set a - flame.
4. Bless - ed be the name of Je - sus! I'm so glad He took me in.

I o-beyed the Spir - it's woo - ing When He said, "Wilt thou be clean?"
My am- bi - tions, plans, and wish - es At my feet in ash - es lay.
I shall nev - er cease to praise Him. Glo - ry, glo - ry to His name!
He's for - giv - en my trans - gres - sions; He has cleansed my heart from sin.

REFRAIN

I will praise Him! I will praise Him! Praise the Lamb for sinners slain!

for sinners slain!

Give Him glo-ry, all ye peo-ple, For His blood can wash a - way each stain.

39 The Solid Rock

SOLID ROCK

Edward Mote, 1797-1874

William B. Bradbury, 1816-1868

1. My hope is built on noth-ing less Than Je-sus' blood and
2. When dark-ness seems to hide His face, I rest on His un-
3. His oath, His cov-e-nant, His blood, Sup-port me in the
4. When He shall come with trum-pet sound, Oh, may I then in

righ-teous-ness. I dare not trust the sweet-est frame, But
chang-ing grace. In ev-'ry high and storm-y gale, My
whelm-ing flood. When all a-round my soul gives way, He
Him be found! Dressed in His righ-teous-ness a-lone, Fault-

REFRAIN

whol-ly lean on Je-sus' name.
an-chor holds with-in the veil.
then is all my Hope and Stay.
less to stand be-fore the throne!

On Christ, the sol-id Rock, I stand; All

oth-er ground is sink-ing sand. All oth-er ground is sink-ing sand.

40 Glory to His Name

Elisha A. Hoffman, 1839 - 1929

John H. Stockton, 1813 - 1877

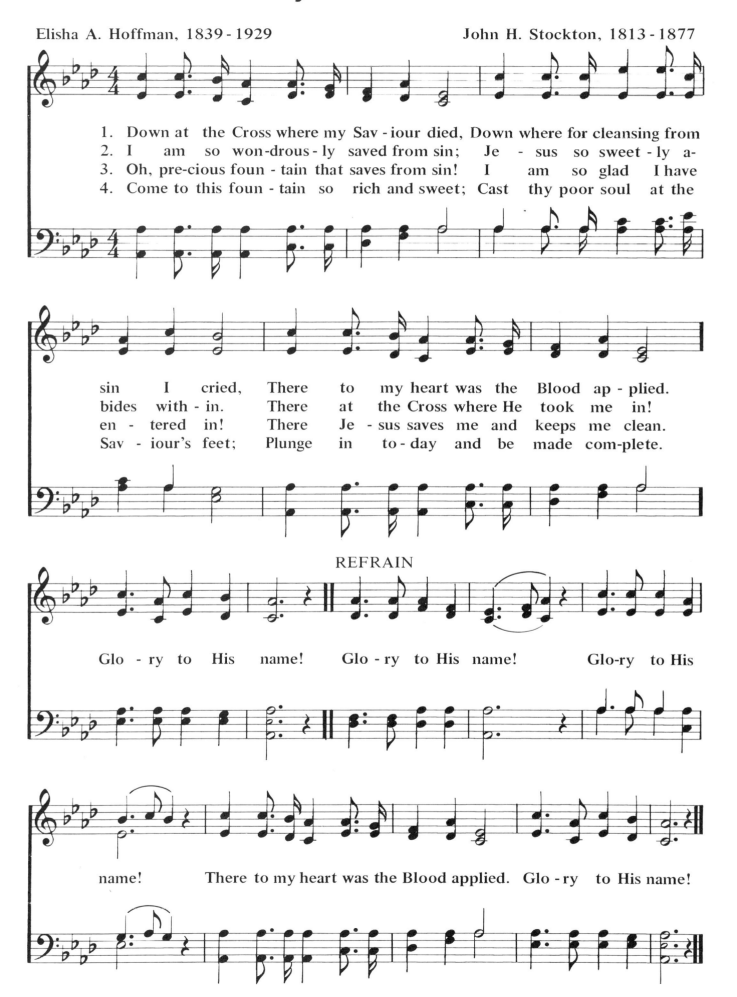

1. Down at the Cross where my Sav-iour died, Down where for cleansing from
2. I am so won-drous-ly saved from sin; Je - sus so sweet-ly a-
3. Oh, pre-cious foun - tain that saves from sin! I am so glad I have
4. Come to this foun - tain so rich and sweet; Cast thy poor soul at the

sin I cried, There to my heart was the Blood ap-plied.
bides with - in. There at the Cross where He took me in!
en - tered in! There Je - sus saves me and keeps me clean.
Sav - iour's feet; Plunge in to - day and be made com-plete.

REFRAIN

Glo - ry to His name! Glo - ry to His name! Glo - ry to His

name! There to my heart was the Blood applied. Glo - ry to His name!

41 I Will Sing the Wondrous Story

WONDROUS STORY

Francis H. Rowley, 1854 - 1952

Peter P. Bilhorn, 1865 - 1936

1. I will sing the won-drous sto - ry Of the Christ who died for me,
2. I was lost, but Je - sus found me, Found the sheep that went a - stray,
3. I was bruised, but Je - sus healed me; Faint was I from many a fall.
4. Days of dark-ness still come o'er me; Sor-row's paths I of - ten tread.
5. He will keep me till the riv - er Rolls its wa - ters at my feet;

How He left His home in glo - ry For the cross of Cal - va - ry.
Threw His lov - ing arms a - round me, Drew me back in - to His way.
Sight was gone, and fears pos-sessed me, But He freed me from them all.
But the Sav - iour still is with me; By His hand I'm safe - ly led.
Then He'll bear me safe - ly o - ver, Where the loved ones I shall meet.

REFRAIN

Yes, I'll sing the won-drous sto - ry Of the
Yes, I'll sing the won-drous sto - ry

Christ who died for me; Sing it with the saints in
of the Christ who died for me; Sing it with

glo - ry, Gath-ered by the crys-tal sea.
the saints in glo - ry, Gathered by the crys-tal sea.

42

O How I Love Jesus

Frederick Whitfield, 1829-1904

Traditional Melody

1. There is a name I love to hear; I love to sing its worth. It sounds like
2. It tells me of a Saviour's love, Who died to set me free. It tells me
3. It tells me what my Father hath In store for ev-'ry day And, tho' I
4. It tells of One whose loving heart Can feel my deep-est woe, Who in each

REFRAIN

mu - sic in mine ear, The sweet-est name on earth.
of His precious blood, The sin-ner's per-fect plea.
tread a darksome path, Yields sunshine all the way.
sor - row bears a part That none can bear be-low.

O how I love Je-sus!

O how I love Je - sus! O how I love Je-sus, Be-cause He first loved me!

43

Jesus Calls Us

GALILEE

Cecil F. Alexander, 1818-1895

William H. Jude, 1851-1922

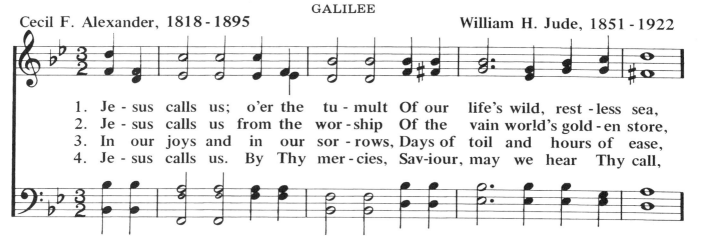

1. Je - sus calls us; o'er the tu - mult Of our life's wild, rest-less sea,
2. Je - sus calls us from the wor-ship Of the vain world's gold-en store,
3. In our joys and in our sor-rows, Days of toil and hours of ease,
4. Je - sus calls us. By Thy mer-cies, Sav-iour, may we hear Thy call,

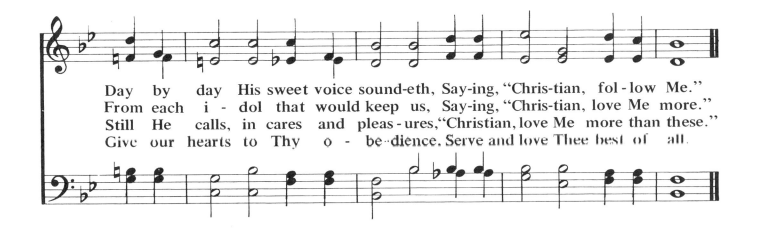

Day by day His sweet voice sound-eth, Say-ing, "Chris-tian, fol-low Me."
From each i - dol that would keep us, Say-ing, "Chris-tian, love Me more."
Still He calls, in cares and pleas-ures, "Christian, love Me more than these."
Give our hearts to Thy o - be-dience. Serve and love Thee best of all.

44   All for Jesus

Mary D. James, 19th Century   Asa Hull, b. 1828

1. All   for Je - sus! all for Je - sus!   All   my be-ing's ransomed pow'rs:
2. Let   my hands perform His bid - ding;   Let   my feet run in His ways;
3. Since my eyes were fixed on Je - sus,   I've lost sight of all be - side,
4. Oh, what won-der! how a - maz - ing!   Je - sus, glo-rious King of Kings,

All   my tho'ts and words and do - ings,   All   my days and all my hours.
Let   my eyes see Je - sus on - ly;   Let   my lips speak forth His praise.
So   en-chained my spir-it's vi - sion,   Look - ing at the Cru - ci - fied.
Deigns to call me His be - lov - ed,   Lets me rest be-neath His wings.

All for Je-sus! all for Je - sus!   All   my days and all my hours; hours.
All for Je-sus! all for Je - sus!   Let my lips speak forth His praise; praise.
All for Je-sus! all for Je - sus!   Look-ing at the Cru - ci - fied; fied.
All for Je-sus! all for Je - sus!   Rest-ing now be - neath His wings; wings.

45 The Beautiful Garden of Prayer

Eleanor Allen Schroll

James H. Fillmore

1. There's a gar-den where Je-sus is wait-ing. There's a place that is
2. There's a gar-den where Je-sus is wait-ing, And I go with my
3. There's a gar-den where Je-sus is wait-ing, And He bids you to

won-drous-ly fair, For it glows with the light of His pres-ence.
bur-den and care, Just to learn from His lips words of com-fort
come, meet Him there; Just to bow and re-ceive a new bless-ing

REFRAIN

'Tis the beau-ti-ful gar-den of prayer.
In the beau-ti-ful gar-den of prayer. Oh, the beau-ti-ful gar-den, the
In the beau-ti-ful gar-den of prayer.

gar-den of prayer! Oh, the beau-ti-ful gar-den of prayer! There my Sav-iour a-

waits, and He o-pens the gates To the beau-ti-ful gar-den of prayer.

46 O to Be like Thee

Thomas O. Chisholm, 1866 - 1960   CHRISTLIKE   William J. Kirkpatrick, 1838 - 1921

1. Oh, to be like Thee! bless-ed Re-deem-er, This is my con-stant
2. Oh, to be like Thee! full of com-pas-sion, Lov-ing, for-giv-ing,
3. Oh, to be like Thee! low-ly in spir-it, Ho-ly and harm-less,
4. Oh, to be like Thee! Lord, I am com-ing, Now to re-ceive th'a-
5. Oh, to be like Thee! While I am plead-ing, Pour out Thy Spir-it,

long-ing and prayer. Glad-ly I'll for-feit all of earth's treas-ures,
ten-der and kind, Help-ing the help-less, cheer-ing the faint-ing,
pa-tient and brave; Meek-ly en-dur-ing cru-el re-proach-es,
noint-ing di-vine. All that I am and have I am bring-ing.
fill with Thy love. Make me a tem-ple meet for Thy dwell-ing;

REFRAIN

Je-sus, Thy per-fect like-ness to wear.
Seek-ing the wan-d'ring sin-ner to find!
Will-ing to suf-fer oth-ers to save.   Oh, to be like Thee!
Lord, from this mo-ment all shall be Thine.
Fit me for life and heav-en a-bove.

Oh, to be like Thee, Bless-ed Re-deem-er, pure as Thou art! Come in Thy

sweet-ness, come in Thy full-ness; Stamp Thine own im-age deep on my heart.

47 I Am Thine, O Lord

Fanny J. Crosby, 1820-1915

William H. Doane, 1832-1915

1. I am Thine, O Lord; I have heard Thy voice, And it told Thy
2. Con-se-crate me now to Thy ser-vice, Lord, By the pow'r of
3. Oh, the pure de-light of a sin-gle hour That be-fore Thy
4. There are depths of love that I can-not know Till I cross the

love to me. But I long to rise in the arms of faith, And be
grace di-vine. Let my soul look up with a stead-fast hope, And my
throne I spend, When I kneel in prayer and with Thee, my God, I com-
nar-row sea; There are heights of joy that I may not reach Till I

REFRAIN

clos-er drawn to Thee.
will be lost in Thine.
mune as friend with friend!
rest in peace with Thee.

Draw me near-er, near-er, bless-ed

near-er, near-er,

Lord, To the Cross where Thou hast died. Draw me near-er, near-er,

near-er, bless-ed Lord, To Thy pre-cious, bleed-ing side.

48 All That Thrills My Soul

HARRIS

Thoro Harris, 1874-1955

Thoro Harris, 1874-1955

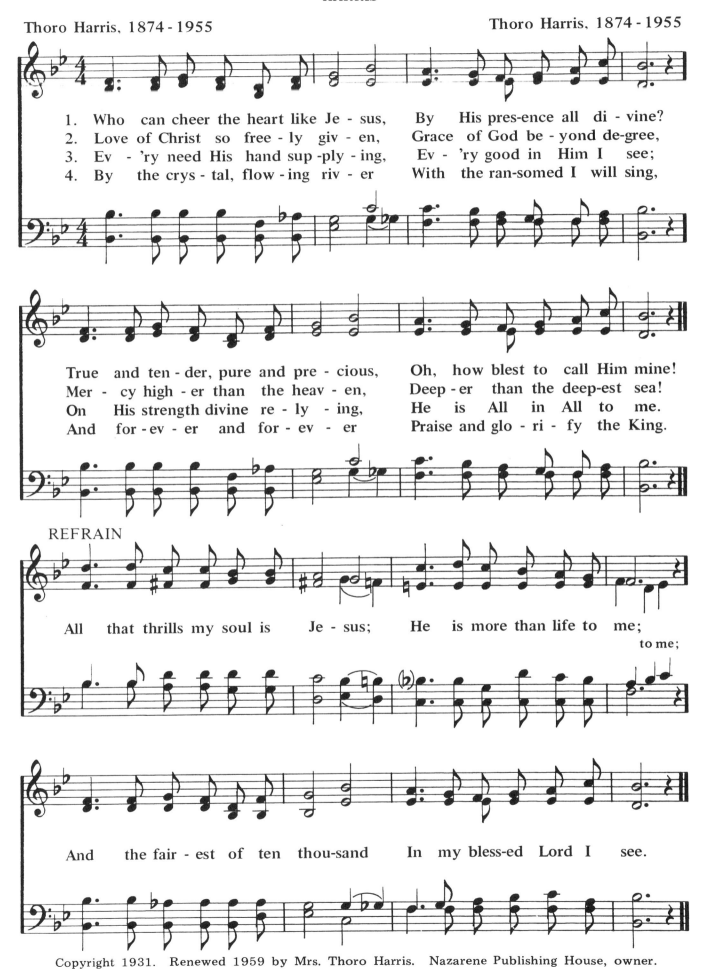

1. Who can cheer the heart like Je - sus, By His pres-ence all di - vine?
2. Love of Christ so free - ly giv - en, Grace of God be - yond de-gree,
3. Ev - 'ry need His hand sup -ply - ing, Ev - 'ry good in Him I see;
4. By the crys - tal, flow -ing riv - er With the ran-somed I will sing,

True and ten - der, pure and pre - cious, Oh, how blest to call Him mine!
Mer - cy high - er than the heav - en, Deep - er than the deep-est sea!
On His strength divine re - ly - ing, He is All in All to me.
And for - ev - er and for - ev - er Praise and glo - ri - fy the King.

REFRAIN

All that thrills my soul is Je - sus; He is more than life to me;
to me;

And the fair - est of ten thou-sand In my bless-ed Lord I see.

49

We Gather Together

KREMSER

Anonymous
Tr. by Theodore Baker, 1851-1934

Folk Song of the Netherlands
Arr. by Edward Kremser, 1838-1914

1. We gath-er to-geth-er to ask the Lord's bless-ing.
2. Be-side us to guide us, our God with us join-ing,
3. We all do ex-tol Thee, Thou Lead-er tri-um-phant,

He chas-tens and has-tens His will to make known.
Or-dain-ing, main-tain-ing His king-dom di-vine;
And pray that Thou still our De-fend-er wilt be.

The wick-ed op-press-ing now cease from dis-tress-ing.
So from the be-gin-ning the fight we were win-ning.
Let Thy con-gre-ga-tion es-cape trib-u-la-tion.

Sing prais-es to His name; He for-gets not His own.
Thou, Lord, wast at our side— all glo-ry be Thine!
Thy name be ev-er praised. O Lord, make us free!

50 Great Is Thy Faithfulness

FAITHFULNESS

Thomas O. Chisholm, 1866 - 1960   William M. Runyan, 1870 - 1957

1. Great is Thy faith-ful-ness, O God, my Fa - ther; There is no shad-ow of
2. Sum - mer and win - ter, and spring-time and harvest, Sun, moon, and stars in their
3. Par - don for sin and a peace that en - dur - eth, Thy own dear presence to

turn - ing with Thee. Thou chang-est not; Thy com - pas - sions, they fail not;
cours - es a - bove, Join with all na - ture in man - i - fold wit-ness
cheer and to guide; Strength for to - day and bright hope for to - mor-row—

REFRAIN

As Thou hast been Thou for - ev - er wilt be.
To Thy great faith-ful - ness, mer - cy, and love. Great is Thy faith-ful-ness!
Bless-ings all mine, with ten thou-sand be - side!

Great is Thy faithfulness! Morning by morning new mercies I see; All I have

rall.

need - ed Thy hand hath provided. Great is Thy faithfulness, Lord, un-to me!

51 Sweet Hour of Prayer

SWEET HOUR

Attrib. to William W. Walford, 1772-1850   William B. Bradbury, 1816-1868

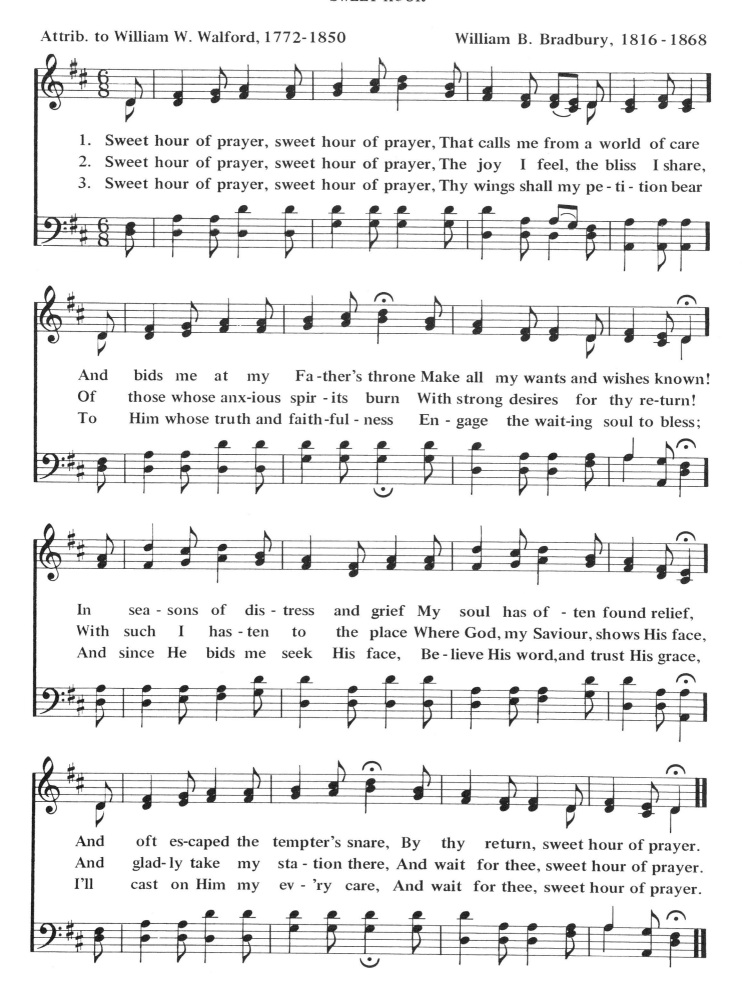

1. Sweet hour of prayer, sweet hour of prayer, That calls me from a world of care
2. Sweet hour of prayer, sweet hour of prayer, The joy I feel, the bliss I share,
3. Sweet hour of prayer, sweet hour of prayer, Thy wings shall my pe - ti - tion bear

And bids me at my Fa-ther's throne Make all my wants and wishes known!
Of those whose anx-ious spir - its burn With strong desires for thy re-turn!
To Him whose truth and faith-ful - ness En - gage the wait-ing soul to bless;

In sea - sons of dis - tress and grief My soul has of - ten found relief,
With such I has - ten to the place Where God, my Saviour, shows His face,
And since He bids me seek His face, Be - lieve His word, and trust His grace,

And oft es-caped the tempter's snare, By thy return, sweet hour of prayer.
And glad-ly take my sta - tion there, And wait for thee, sweet hour of prayer.
I'll cast on Him my ev - 'ry care, And wait for thee, sweet hour of prayer.

52 God Leads Us Along

G. A. Young, 19th Century

G. A. Young, 19th Century

1. In shad-y green pas-tures so rich and so sweet, God leads His dear
2. Some times on the mount where the sun shines so bright, God leads His dear
3. Tho' sor-rows be-fall us and Sa-tan op-pose, God leads His dear
4. A - way from the mire, and a - way from the clay, God leads His dear

chil-dren a - long. Where the wa-ter's cool flow bathes the wea-ry one's feet,
chil-dren a - long. Some-times in the val - ley in the dark-est of night,
chil-dren a - long. Through grace we can con - quer, de - feat all our foes.
chil-dren a - long. A - way up in glo - ry, e - ter-ni-ty's day,

REFRAIN

God leads His dear children a - long. Some thro' the waters, some thro' the flood,

Some thro' the fire, but all thro' the Blood. Some thro' great sor-row, but

rit.

God gives a song In the night sea-son and all the day long.

53 Saviour, like a Shepherd Lead Us

BRADBURY

Ascribed to Dorothy A. Thrupp, 1779 - 1847   William B. Bradbury, 1816 - 1868

1. Sav - iour, like a shep-herd lead   us; Much we need Thy ten-der care.
2. We are Thine; do Thou be-friend   us; Be the Guard-ian of our way.
3. Thou hast promised to re - ceive   us, Poor and sin - ful tho' we be;
4. Ear - ly let us seek Thy fa - vor; Ear - ly let us do Thy will.

In Thy pleas-ant pas-tures feed   us; For our use Thy folds pre-pare.
Keep Thy flock; from sin de - fend   us; Seek us when we go a - stray.
Thou hast mer-cy to re - lieve   us, Grace to cleanse, and power to free.
Bless - ed Lord and on - ly Sav - iour, With Thy love our bos-oms fill.

Bless - ed Je - sus, bless-ed Je - sus! Thou hast bought us; Thine we are.
Bless - ed Je - sus, bless-ed Je - sus! Hear, O hear us, when we pray.
Bless - ed Je - sus, bless-ed Je - sus! We will ear - ly turn to Thee.
Bless - ed Je - sus, bless-ed Je - sus! Thou hast loved us; love us still.

Bless - ed Je - sus, bless-ed Je - sus! Thou hast bought us; Thine we are.
Bless - ed Je - sus, bless-ed Je - sus! Hear, O hear us, when we pray.
Bless - ed Je - sus, bless-ed Je - sus! We will ear - ly turn to Thee.
Bless - ed Je - sus, bless-ed Je - sus! Thou hast loved us; love us still.

54 Jesus Will Walk with Me

Haldor Lillenas, 1885 - 1959   Haldor Lillenas, 1885 - 1959

1. Je - sus will walk with me down thro' the val-ley; Je - sus will walk with me
2. Je - sus will walk with me when I am tempt-ed, Giv-ing me strength as my
3. Je - sus will walk with me, guarding me ev - er, Giv-ing me vic - t'ry thro'
4. Je - sus will walk with me in life's fair morning, And when the shadows of

o - ver the plain. When in the shad-ow or when in the sun-shine,
need may de - mand. When in af - flic - tion His pres - ence is near me;
storm and thro' strife. He is my Com-fort-er, Coun-sel - or, Lead-er,
eve-ning must come. Liv - ing or dy - ing, He will not for-sake me.

REFRAIN

If He goes with me I shall not com-plain. Je - sus will
I am up - held by His al-might-y hand.
O - ver the un - e - ven jour-ney of life.
Je - sus will walk with me all the way home.   Je - sus, my Sav - iour, will

walk with me. He will talk with me; He will walk with me. In joy or in

sor-row, to - day and to - mor-row, I know He will walk with me._____
will walk with me.

Copyright 1922. Renewed 1950 by Lillenas Publishing Co.

55

He Leadeth Me

Joseph H. Gilmore, 1834 - 1918

William B. Bradbury, 1816 - 1868

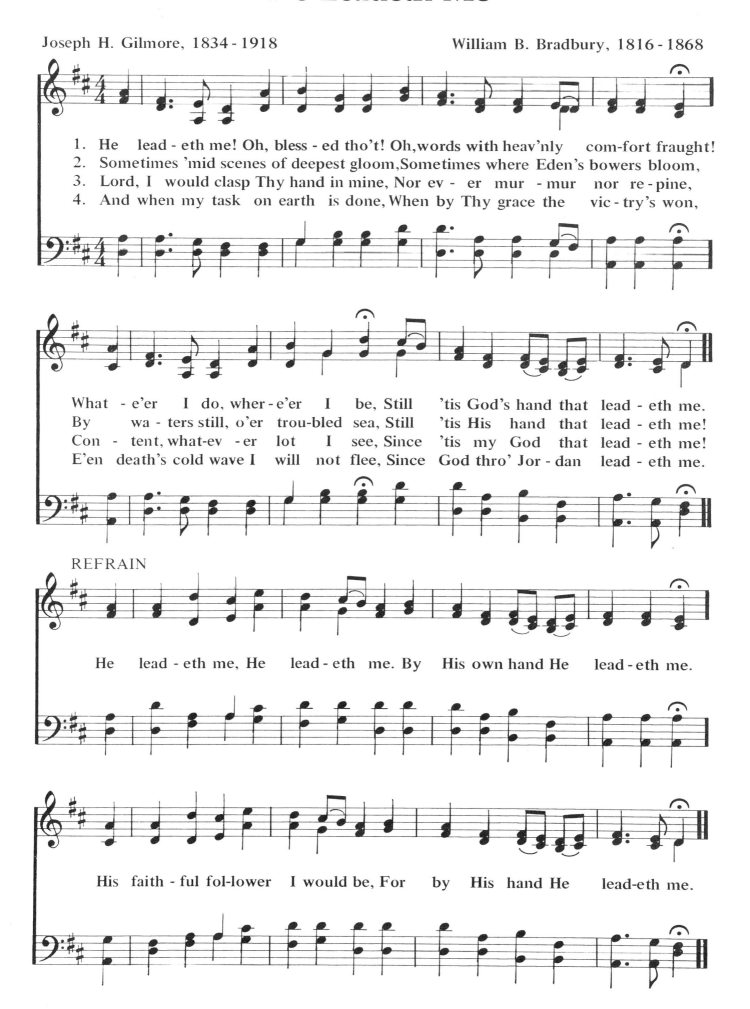

1. He lead-eth me! Oh, bless-ed tho't! Oh, words with heav'nly com-fort fraught!
2. Sometimes 'mid scenes of deepest gloom, Sometimes where Eden's bowers bloom,
3. Lord, I would clasp Thy hand in mine, Nor ev - er mur - mur nor re-pine,
4. And when my task on earth is done, When by Thy grace the vic-try's won,

What - e'er I do, wher-e'er I be, Still 'tis God's hand that lead-eth me.
By wa - ters still, o'er trou-bled sea, Still 'tis His hand that lead - eth me!
Con - tent, what-ev - er lot I see, Since 'tis my God that lead - eth me!
E'en death's cold wave I will not flee, Since God thro' Jor - dan lead - eth me.

REFRAIN

He lead - eth me, He lead-eth me. By His own hand He lead-eth me.

His faith - ful fol-lower I would be, For by His hand He lead-eth me.

56 All the Way My Saviour Leads

ALL THE WAY

Fanny J. Crosby, 1820 - 1915

Robert Lowry, 1826 - 1899

1. All the way my Sav-iour leads me. What have I to ask be-side?
2. All the way my Sav-iour leads me, Cheers each wind-ing path I tread,
3. All the way my Sav-iour leads me. Oh, the full-ness of His love!

Can I doubt His ten-der mer-cy Who thro' life has been my Guide?
Gives me grace for ev-'ry tri-al, Feeds me with the liv-ing bread.
Per-fect rest to me is prom-ised In my Fa-ther's house a-bove.

Heav'nly peace, di-vin-est com-fort, Here by faith in Him to dwell!
Tho' my wea-ry steps may fal-ter, And my soul a-thirst may be,
When my spir-it, clothed, im-mor-tal, Wings its flight to realms of day,

For I know, what-e'er be-fall me, Je-sus do-eth all things well.
Gush-ing from the Rock be-fore me, Lo! a spring of joy I see.
This my song thro' end-less a-ges— Je-sus led me all the way;

For I know, what-e'er be-fall me, Je-sus do-eth all things well.
Gush-ing from the Rock be-fore me, Lo! a spring of joy I see.
This my song thro' end-less a-ges— Je-sus led me all the way.

57 Lead, Kindly Light

LUX BENIGNA

John H. Newman, 1801 - 1890   John B. Dykes, 1823 - 1876

1. Lead, kind-ly Light, a - mid th'en-cir-cling gloom;   Lead Thou me on!
2. I was not ev - er thus, nor prayed that Thou   Shouldst lead me on;
3. So long Thy power hath blest me, sure it still   Will lead me on

The night is dark, and I am far from home;   Lead Thou me on!
I loved to choose and see my path, but now   Lead Thou me on!
O'er moor and fen, o'er crag and tor-rent, till   The night is gone,

Keep Thou my feet; I do not ask to see ----
I loved the gar - ish day, and, spite of fears, ---
And with the morn those an - gel fac - es smile ----

The dis - tant scene; one step e - nough for me.
Pride ruled my will. Re - mem - ber not past years.
Which I have loved long since and lost a - while!

58 Trust and Obey

John H. Sammis, 1849-1919   Daniel B. Towner, 1850-1919

1. When we walk with the Lord In the light of His Word, What a glo - ry He
2. Not a shad - ow can rise, Not a cloud in the skies, But His smile quickly
3. Not a bur - den we bear, Not a sor - row we share But our toil He doth
4. But we nev - er can prove The de-lights of His love Un - til all on the
5. Then in fel - low - ship sweet We will sit at His feet, Or we'll walk by His

sheds on our way! While we do His good will, He a - bides with us still,
drives it a - way. Not a doubt nor a fear, Not a sigh nor a tear
rich - ly re - pay. Not a grief nor a loss, Not a frown nor a cross
al - tar we lay; For the fa - vor He shows And the joy He be-stows
side in the way. What He says we will do; Where He sends we will go;

REFRAIN

And with all who will trust and o - bey.
Can a - bide while we trust and o - bey.
But is blest if we trust and o - bey.   Trust and o - bey, For there's
Are for them who will trust and o - bey.
Nev - er fear, on - ly trust and o - bey.

no oth - er way To be hap-py in Je - sus But to trust and o - bey.

59

Nearer, Still Nearer

MORRIS

Lelia N. Morris, 1862-1929

Lelia N. Morris, 1862-1929

1. Near-er, still near-er, close to Thy heart, Draw me, my Sav-iour—so pre-
2. Near-er, still near-er, noth-ing I bring, Naught as an of-f'ring to Je-
3. Near-er, still near-er, Lord, to be Thine! Sin, with its fol-lies, I glad-
4. Near-er, still near-er, while life shall last, Till safe in glo-ry my an-

cious Thou art! Fold me, oh, fold me close to Thy breast. Shel-ter me safe
sus, my King; On - ly my sin - ful, now contrite heart. Grant me the cleans-
ly re - sign, All of its pleas-ures, pomp and its pride. Give me but Je-
chor is cast; Thro' endless a - ges ev - er to be Near-er, my Sav-

in that "Ha - ven of Rest"; Shel - ter me safe in that "Ha - ven of Rest."
ing Thy blood doth im - part; Grant me the cleans-ing Thy blood doth impart.
sus, my Lord, cru - ci - fied; Give me but Je - sus, my Lord, cru - ci-fied.
iour, still near - er to Thee; Near - er, my Sav-iour, still near - er to Thee!

60

Faith of Our Fathers

ST. CATHERINE

Henri F. Hemy, 1818-1888
Adapt. by James G. Walton, 1821-1905

Frederick W. Faber, 1814-1863

1. Faith of our fa - thers, liv - ing still In spite of dun-geon, fire, and sword!
2. Our fa-thers, chained in pris-ons dark, Were still in heart and conscience free.
3. Faith of our fa - thers! we will love Both friend and foe in all our strife;

Oh, how our hearts beat high with joy When-e'er we hear that glo - rious word!
How sweet would be their children's fate If they, like them, could die for thee!
And preach thee, too, as love knows how, By kind-ly words and vir - tuous life.

Faith of our fa - thers! ho - ly faith! We will be true to thee till death!

61   I Would Be True

PEEK

Howard Arnold Walter, 1883 - 1918

Author of third stanza unknown

Joseph Yates Peek, 1843 - 1911

1. I would be true, for there are those who trust me. I would be pure, for there
2. I would be friend of all— the foe, the friend-less. I would be giv - ing, and
3. I would be prayerful thro' each bus - y mo - ment. I would be con - stant-ly

are those who care. I would be strong, for there is much to suf - fer. I would be
for - get the gift. I would be hum - ble, for I know my weak-ness. I would look
in touch with God. I would be tuned to hear His slightest whis-per. I would have

brave, for there is much to dare. I would be brave, for there is much to dare.
up, and laugh, and love, and lift. I would look up, and laugh, and love, and lift.
faith to keep the path Christ trod. I would have faith to keep the path Christ trod.

62 Near to the Heart of God

Cleland B. McAfee, 1866-1944

Cleland B. McAfee, 1866-1944

1. There is a place of qui-et rest, Near to the heart of God;
2. There is a place of com-fort sweet, Near to the heart of God;
3. There is a place of full re-lease, Near to the heart of God;

A place where sin can-not mo-lest, Near to the heart of God.
A place where we our Sav-iour meet, Near to the heart of God.
A place where all is joy and peace, Near to the heart of God.

REFRAIN

O Je-sus, blest Re-deem-er, Sent from the heart of God,

Hold us, who wait be-fore Thee, Near to the heart of God.

63 In the Cross of Christ

John Bowring, 1792-1872

RATHBUN

Ithamar Conkey, 1815-1867

1. In the cross of Christ I glo-ry, Tow'r-ing o'er the wrecks of time.
2. When the woes of life o'er-take me, Hopes de-ceive, and fears an-noy,
3. When the sun of bliss is beam-ing Light and love up-on my way,
4. Bane and bless-ing, pain and pleas-ure, By the Cross are sanc-ti-fied;

All the light of sa - cred sto - ry   Gath-ers round its   head sub - lime.
Nev - er   shall the Cross   for - sake me.   Lo! it glows with peace and   joy.
From the Cross the   ra - diance stream-ing   Adds more lus - ter   to   the   day.
Peace is   there that knows no   meas - ure,   Joys that thro' all   time   a - bide.

64   Have Thine Own Way, Lord

POLLARD

Adelaide A. Pollard, 1862 - 1934   George C. Stebbins, 1846 - 1945

1. Have Thine own way, Lord! Have Thine own   way!   Thou   art   the
2. Have Thine own way, Lord! Have Thine own   way!   Search   me   and
3. Have Thine own way, Lord! Have Thine own   way!   Wound-ed   and
4. Have Thine own way, Lord! Have Thine own   way!   Hold   o'er   my

Pot - ter;   I   am   the   clay.   Mold me and make   me af - ter Thy
try   me, Mas - ter, to - day!   Whit - er   than snow, Lord, wash me just
wea - ry, help me, I   pray!   Pow - er— all pow - er— sure - ly is
be - ing ab - so - lute sway!   Fill with Thy Spir - it   till all shall

will,   While I am   wait - ing, yield - ed   and   still.
now,   As   in Thy   pres - ence hum - bly   I   bow.
Thine!   Touch me and   heal   me, Sav - iour di - vine!
see   Christ on - ly,   al - ways liv - ing   in   me!

65 I Will Sing of My Redeemer

Philip P. Bliss, 1838-1876

James McGranahan, 1840-1907

1. I will sing of my Re-deem-er And His won-drous love to me;
2. I will tell the won-drous sto-ry, How, my lost es-tate to save,
3. I will praise my dear Re-deem-er; His tri-um-phant pow'r I'll tell,
4. I will sing of my Re-deem-er And His heav'n-ly love to me;

On the cru-el Cross He suf-fered, From the curse to set me free.
In His bound-less love and mer-cy He the ran-som free-ly gave.
How the vic-to-ry He giv-eth O-ver sin, and death, and hell.
He from death to life hath bro't me, Son of God, with Him to be.

REFRAIN

Sing, oh, sing _____ of my Re-deem-er. With His
Sing, oh, sing of my Re-deem-er; Sing, oh, sing of my Re-deem-er. With His

blood _____ He pur-chased me. _____ On the Cross _____ He
blood He purchased me; With His blood He purchased me. On the Cross He sealed my par-don;

sealed my par-don, Paid the debt _____ and made me free. _____
On the Cross He sealed my pardon, Paid the debt and made me free, and made me free.

66 My Wonderful Lord

Haldor Lillenas, 1885 - 1959

Haldor Lillenas, 1885 - 1959

1. I have found a deep peace that I nev-er had known And a joy this world
2. I de - sire that my life shall be or-dered by Thee, That my will be in
3. All the tal - ents I have I have laid at Thy feet; Thy ap-prov - al shall
4. Thou art fair - er to me than the fair - est of earth, Thou om-nip - o-tent,

could not af - ford   Since I yield - ed con-trol of my bod - y and soul
per - fect ac - cord   With Thine own sov'reign will, Thy de-sires to ful - fill,
be my re - ward.   Be my store great or small, I sur - ren - der it all
life - giv - ing Word.   O Thou An-cient of Days, Thou art wor - thy all praise,

REFRAIN

To my won - der-ful, won - der-ful Lord.
My won - der-ful, won - der-ful Lord.
To my won - der-ful, won - der-ful Lord.
My won - der-ful, won - der-ful Lord!

My won - der-ful Lord, my

won - der - ful Lord, By an - gels and ser - aphs in heav - en a - dored! I

bow at Thy shrine, my Sav-iour di-vine, My won-der-ful, won-der-ful Lord.

67 Close to Thee

Fanny J. Crosby, 1820-1915

Silas J. Vail, 1818-1884

1. Thou, my ev-er-last-ing por-tion, More than friend or life to me,
2. Not for ease or world-ly pleas-ure Nor for fame my prayer shall be.
3. Lead me thro' the vale of shad-ows; Bear me o'er life's fit-ful sea;

Fine

D.S.—All a-long my pil-grim jour-ney, Sav-iour, let me walk with Thee.
D.S.—Glad-ly will I toil and suf-fer; On-ly let me walk with Thee.
D.S.—Then the gate of life e-ter-nal May I en-ter, Lord, with Thee.

REFRAIN

D.S.

Close to Thee, close to Thee, Close to Thee, close to Thee;

68 O Master, Let Me Walk with Thee

MARYTON

Washington Gladden, 1836-1918

H. Percy Smith, 1825-1898

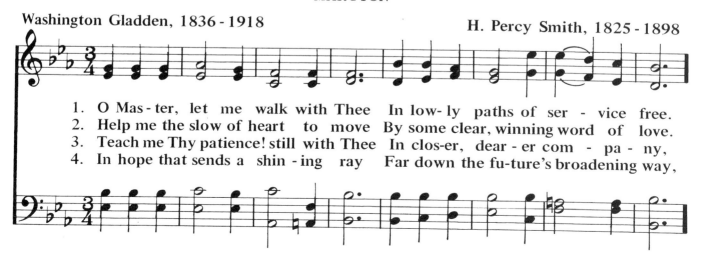

1. O Mas-ter, let me walk with Thee In low-ly paths of ser-vice free.
2. Help me the slow of heart to move By some clear, winning word of love.
3. Teach me Thy patience! still with Thee In clos-er, dear-er com-pa-ny,
4. In hope that sends a shin-ing ray Far down the fu-ture's broadening way,

Tell me Thy se - cret; help me bear The strain of toil, the fret of care.
Teach me the way-ward feet to stay, And guide them in the home-ward way.
In work that keeps faith sweet and strong, In trust that tri - umphs o - ver wrong.
In peace that on - ly Thou canst give, With Thee, O Mas - ter, let me live.

69 My Jesus, I Love Thee

GORDON

William R. Featherstone, 1842 - 1878

Adoniram J. Gordon, 1836 - 1895

1. My Je - sus, I love Thee; I know Thou art mine. For Thee all the
2. I love Thee be-cause Thou hast first lov - ed me, And pur-chased my
3. I will love Thee in life, I will love Thee in death, And praise Thee as
4. In man-sions of glo - ry and end-less de - light, I'll ev - er a -

fol - lies of sin I re - sign. My gra - cious Re-deem - er, my
par - don on Cal - va - ry's tree. I love Thee for wear - ing the
long as Thou lend - est me breath; And say when the death-dew lies
dore Thee in heav - en so bright. I'll sing with the glit - ter - ing

Sav - iour art Thou. If ev - er I loved Thee, my Je - sus, 'tis now.
thorns on Thy brow. If ev - er I loved Thee, my Je - sus, 'tis now.
cold on my brow, "If ev - er I loved Thee, my Je - sus, 'tis now."
crown on my brow, "If ev - er I loved Thee, my Je - sus, 'tis now."

70 Jesus, Lover of My Soul

MARTYN

Charles Wesley, 1707-1788

Simeon B. Marsh, 1798-1875

1. Je - sus, Lov - er of my soul, Let me to Thy bos - om fly,
2. Oth - er ref - uge have I none; Hangs my help-less soul on Thee.
3. Thou, O Christ, art all I want; More than all in Thee I find.
4. Plen-teous grace with Thee is found, Grace to cov - er all my sin.

While the near - er wa - ters roll, While the tem - pest still is high!
Leave, ah, leave me not a - lone; Still sup-port and com - fort me!
Raise the fall - en, cheer the faint, Heal the sick, and lead the blind.
Let the heal - ing streams a-bound; Make and keep me pure with - in.

Hide me, O my Sav - iour, hide, Till the storm of life is past.
All my trust on Thee is stayed; All my help from Thee I bring.
Just and ho - ly is Thy name; I am all un - righ-teous-ness.
Thou of life the Foun-tain art; Free - ly let me take of Thee.

Safe in - to the ha - ven guide. Oh, re - ceive my soul at last!
Cov - er my de - fense-less head With the shad-ow of Thy wing.
False and full of sin I am; Thou art full of truth and grace.
Spring Thou up with - in my heart; Rise to all e - ter - ni - ty.

71 More About Jesus

SWENEY

Eliza E. Hewitt, 1851-1920

John R. Sweney, 1837-1899

1. More a-bout Je-sus would I know, More of His grace to oth - ers show;
2. More a-bout Je-sus let me learn, More of His ho - ly will dis - cern;
3. More a-bout Je-sus in His Word, Hold - ing com-mu-nion with my Lord,
4. More a-bout Je-sus on His throne, Rich - es in glo - ry all His own;

More of His sav - ing full - ness see, More of His love who died for me.
Spir - it of God, my Teach - er be, Show - ing the things of Christ to me.
Hear - ing His voice in ev - 'ry line, Mak - ing each faith-ful say - ing mine.
More of His king - dom's sure in - crease; More of His com-ing, Prince of Peace.

REFRAIN

More, more a - bout Je - sus; More, more a - bout Je - sus;

More of His sav - ing full-ness see, More of His love who died for me.

72 Count Your Blessings

Johnson Oatman, Jr. 1856-1922

Edwin O. Excell, 1851-1921

1. When up-on life's bil-lows you are tem-pest - tossed, When you are dis-
2. Are you ev - er bur-dened with a load of care? Does the cross seem
3. When you look at oth - ers with their lands and gold, Think that Christ has
4. So a - mid the con-flict, wheth-er great or small, Do not be dis-

cour-aged, think-ing all is lost, Count your man-y bless - ings, name them
heav - y you are called to bear? Count your man-y bless - ings; ev - 'ry
prom-ised you His wealth un - told. Count your man-y bless - ings; mon - ey
cour-aged; God is o - ver all. Count your man-y bless - ings; an - gels

one by one, And it will sur - prise you what the Lord hath done.
doubt will fly, And you will be sing - ing as the days go by.
can - not buy Your re-ward in heav - en nor your home on high.
will at - tend, Help and com-fort give you to your jour - ney's end.

REFRAIN

Count your bless - ings; Name them one by one. Count your
Count your man-y bless - ings; Name them one by one. Count your man-y

bless - ings; See what God hath done. Count your bless-ings;
bless - ings; See what God hath done. Count your many bless-ings;

Name them one by one. Count your man-y bless-ings; See what God hath done.

73 'Tis So Sweet to Trust in Jesus

TRUST IN JESUS

Louisa M. R. Stead, 19th Century

William J. Kirkpatrick, 1838 - 1921

1. 'Tis so sweet to trust in Je - sus, Just to take Him at His Word;
2. Oh, how sweet to trust in Je - sus, Just to trust His cleans-ing blood;
3. Yes, 'tis sweet to trust in Je - sus, Just from sin and self to cease;
4. I'm so glad I learned to trust Thee, Pre-cious Je - sus, Sav-iour, Friend;

Just to rest up - on His prom - ise; Just to know, "Thus saith the Lord."
Just in sim - ple faith to plunge me 'Neath the heal - ing, cleans-ing flood!
Just from Je - sus sim - ply tak - ing Life and rest, and joy and peace.
And I know that Thou art with me, Wilt be with me to the end.

REFRAIN

Je - sus, Je - sus, how I trust Him! How I've proved Him o'er and o'er!

Je - sus, Je - sus, pre - cious Je - sus! O for grace to trust Him more!

74 Does Jesus Care?

Frank E. Graeff, 1860-1919

J. Lincoln Hall, 1866-1930

1. Does Je-sus care when my heart is pained Too deep-ly for
2. Does Je-sus care when my way is dark With a name-less
3. Does Je-sus care when I've tried and failed To re-sist some temp-
4. Does Je-sus care when I've said, "Good-by," To the dear-est on

mirth and song, As the bur-dens press, and the cares dis-tress, And the
dread and fear? As the day-light fades in-to deep night shades, Does He
ta-tion strong; When for my deep grief I find no re-lief, Tho' my
earth to me, And my sad heart aches till it near-ly breaks? Is it

REFRAIN

way grows wea-ry and long?
care e-nough to be near?
tears flow all the night long?
aught to Him? Does He see?

Oh, yes, He cares; I know He cares. His

heart is touched with my grief.___ When the days are wea-ry, the

rit.

long nights drea-ry, I know my Sav-iour cares.___

He cares.

75 The Haven of Rest

Henry L. Gilmour, 1837-1920

George D. Moore, 19th Century

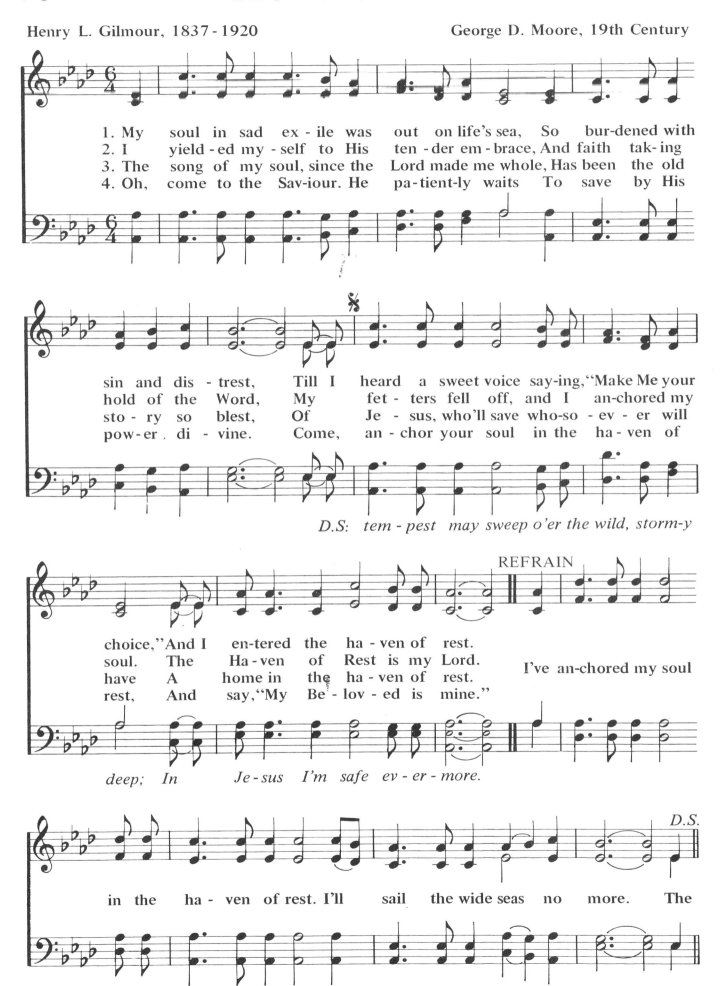

1. My soul in sad ex-ile was out on life's sea, So bur-dened with
2. I yield-ed my-self to His ten-der em-brace, And faith tak-ing
3. The song of my soul, since the Lord made me whole, Has been the old
4. Oh, come to the Sav-iour. He pa-tient-ly waits To save by His

sin and dis-trest, Till I heard a sweet voice say-ing, "Make Me your
hold of the Word, My fet-ters fell off, and I an-chored my
sto-ry so blest, Of Je-sus, who'll save who-so-ev-er will
pow-er di-vine. Come, an-chor your soul in the ha-ven of

D.S: tem-pest may sweep o'er the wild, storm-y

REFRAIN

choice," And I en-tered the ha-ven of rest.
soul. The Ha-ven of Rest is my Lord.   I've an-chored my soul
have A home in the ha-ven of rest.
rest, And say, "My Be-lov-ed is mine."

deep; In Je-sus I'm safe ev-er-more.

in the ha-ven of rest. I'll sail the wide seas no more. The

D.S.

76 God Will Take Care of You

Civilla D. Martin, 1869-1948

W. Stillman Martin, 1862-1935

1. Be not dis-mayed what - e'er be-tide; God will take care of you.
2. Thro' days of toil when heart doth fail; God will take care of you;
3. All you may need He will pro-vide; God will take care of you.
4. No mat-ter what may be the test, God will take care of you.

Be - neath His wings of love a-bide; God will take care of you.
When dan - gers fierce your path as-sail, God will take care of you.
Noth-ing you ask will be de-nied; God will take care of you.
Lean, wea - ry one, up - on His breast; God will take care of you.

REFRAIN

God will take care of you, Thro' ev-'ry day, O'er all the way.

He will take care of you; God will take care of you.

take care of you.

77 Hiding in Thee

HIDING

William O. Cushing, 1823 - 1902

Ira D. Sankey, 1840 - 1908

1. Oh, safe to the Rock that is high - er than I,
2. In the calm of the noon - tide, in sor - row's lone hour,
3. How oft in the con - flict, when pressed by the foe,

My soul in its con - flicts and sor - rows would fly. So
In times when temp - ta - tion casts o'er me its pow'r; In the
I have fled to my Ref - uge and breathed out my woe! How

sin - ful, so wea - ry, Thine, Thine would I be. Thou
tem - pests of life, on its wide, heav - ing sea, Thou
of - ten, when tri - als like sea bil - lows roll, Have I

REFRAIN

blest "Rock of A - ges," I'm hid - ing in Thee.
blest "Rock of A - ges," I'm hid - ing in Thee. Hid - ing in Thee,
hid - den in Thee, O Thou Rock of my soul!

Hid - ing in Thee; Thou blest "Rock of A - ges," I'm hid - ing in Thee.

78

Come, Ye Disconsolate
CONSOLATION

Thomas Moore, 1779-1852
Alt. by Thomas Hastings, 1784-1872

Samuel Webbe, 1740-1816

1. Come, ye dis - con - so - late, wher - e'er ye lan - guish; Come to the
2. Joy of the des - o - late, Light of the stray - ing, Hope of the
3. Here see the Bread of Life; see wa - ters flow - ing Forth from the

mer - cy seat, fer - vent - ly kneel. Here bring your wound - ed hearts;
pen - i - tent, fade - less and pure! Here speaks the Com - fort - er,
throne of God, pure from a - bove. Come to the feast of love;

here tell your an - guish. Earth has no sor - row that Heav'n can - not heal.
ten - der - ly say - ing, "Earth has no sor - row that Heav'n can - not cure."
come, ev - er know - ing Earth has no sor - row but Heav'n can re - move.

79

Now the Day Is Over
MERRIAL

Sabine Baring-Gould, 1834-1924

Joseph Barnby, 1838-1896

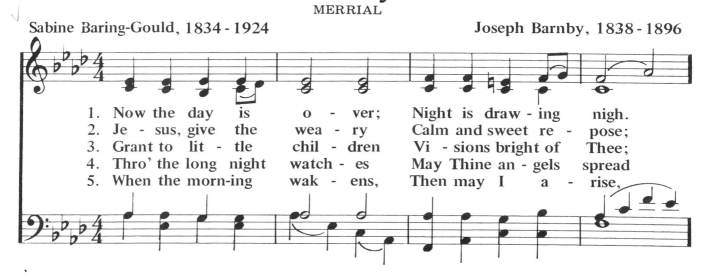

1. Now the day is o - ver; Night is draw - ing nigh.
2. Je - sus, give the wea - ry Calm and sweet re - pose;
3. Grant to lit - tle chil - dren Vi - sions bright of Thee;
4. Thro' the long night watch - es May Thine an - gels spread
5. When the morn - ing wak - ens, Then may I a - rise,

Shad - ows of the eve - ning Steal a-cross the sky.
With Thy ten - d'rest bless - ing May our eye - lids close.
Guard the sail - ors toss - ing On the deep, blue sea.
Their white wings a - bove me, Watch - ing 'round my bed.
Pure and fresh and sin - less In Thy ho - ly eyes.

80 Take Time to Be Holy
HOLINESS

William D. Longstaff, 1822 - 1894   George C. Stebbins, 1846 - 1945

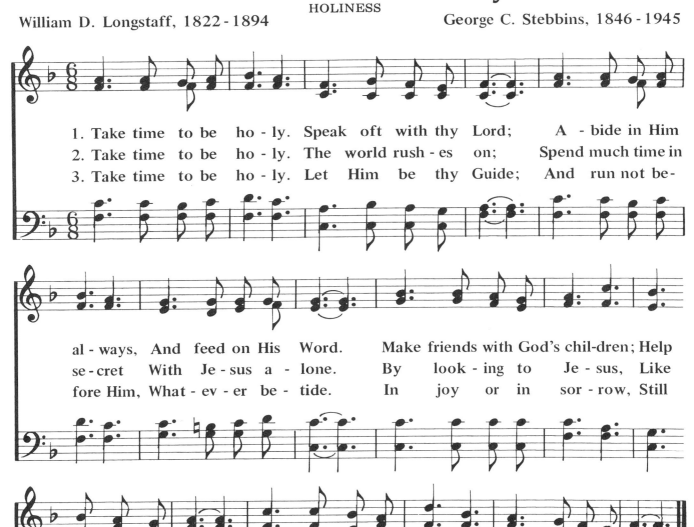

1. Take time to be ho - ly. Speak oft with thy Lord; A - bide in Him
2. Take time to be ho - ly. The world rush - es on; Spend much time in
3. Take time to be ho - ly. Let Him be thy Guide; And run not be-

al - ways, And feed on His Word. Make friends with God's chil-dren; Help
se - cret With Je - sus a - lone. By look - ing to Je - sus, Like
fore Him, What - ev - er be - tide. In joy or in sor - row, Still

those who are weak, For - get - ting in noth - ing His bless-ing to seek.
Him thou shalt be; Thy friends in thy con - duct His likeness shall see.
fol - low thy Lord And, look - ing to Je - sus, Still trust in His Word.

81 Sweet Peace, the Gift of God's Love

SWEET PEACE

Peter P. Bilhorn, 1865-1936

Peter P. Bilhorn, 1865-1936

1. There comes to my heart one sweet strain (sweet strain), A
2. Thro' Christ on the Cross peace was made (was made); My
3. When Je - sus as Lord I had crowned (had crowned), My
4. In Je - sus for peace I a - bide (a - bide); And

glad and a joy - ous re - frain (re - frain); I sing it a -
debt by His death was all paid (all paid). No oth - er foun -
heart with this peace did a - bound (a - bound). In Him the rich
as I keep close to His side (His side), There's noth - ing but

gain and a - gain: Sweet peace,
da - tion is laid For peace, the gift of God's love.
bless - ing I found, Sweet peace,
peace doth be - tide, Sweet peace,

REFRAIN

Peace, peace, sweet peace! Won-der-ful gift from a - bove! a - bove! Oh,

won - der - ful, won-der-ful peace! Sweet peace, the gift of God's love!

82 God Be with You

Jeremiah E. Rankin, 1828 - 1904

William G. Tomer, 1833 - 1896

1. God be with you till we meet a-gain; By His counsels guide, uphold you;
2. God be with you till we meet a-gain, 'Neath His wings protecting hide you,
3. God be with you till we meet a-gain; When life's per-ils thick con-found you,
4. God be with you till we meet a-gain, Keep love's banner floating o'er you,

With His sheep se-cure-ly fold you.
Dai-ly man-na still pro-vide you.
Put His arms un-fail-ing round you.
Smite death's threat'ning wave before you.

God be with you till we meet a-gain.

REFRAIN

Till we meet,— till we meet, Till we meet at Je-sus' feet;
Till we meet, till we meet, till we meet;

Till we meet,— till we meet, God be with you till we meet a-gain.
Till we meet, till we meet,

83 Jesus, Saviour, Pilot Me

PILOT

Edward Hopper, 1816 - 1888

John E. Gould, 1822 - 1875

1. Je - sus, Sav - iour, pi - lot me O - ver life's tem-pes-tuous sea.
2. As a moth - er stills her child, Thou canst hush the o - cean wild;
3. When at last I near the shore, And the fear - ful break-ers roar

Un-known waves be-fore me roll, Hid-ing rocks and treach'rous shoal.
Bois-t'rous waves o - bey Thy will When Thou say'st to them, "Be still!"
'Twixt me and the peace-ful rest, Then, while lean-ing on Thy breast,

Chart and com - pass came from Thee; Je - sus, Sav - iour, pi - lot me.
Won-drous Sov - 'reign of the sea, Je - sus, Sav - iour, pi - lot me.
May I hear Thee say to me, "Fear not, I will pi - lot thee."

84 Blest Be the Tie That Binds

DENNIS

John Fawcett, 1740 - 1817

Hans G. Nageli, 1773 - 1836

1. Blest be the tie that binds Our hearts in Chris - tian love;
2. Be - fore our Fa - ther's throne We pour our ar - dent prayers;
3. We share our mu - tual woes, Our mu - tual bur - dens bear;
4. When we a - sun - der part It gives us in - ward pain;

The fel-low-ship of kin-dred minds Is like to that a-bove.
Our fears, our hopes, our aims are one, Our com-forts and our cares.
And of-ten for each oth-er flows The sym-pa-thiz-ing tear.
But we shall still be joined in heart, And hope to meet a-gain.

85 Wonderful Words of Life

WORDS OF LIFE

Philip P. Bliss, 1838-1876   Philip P. Bliss, 1838-1876

1. Sing them o-ver a-gain to me, Won-der-ful words of Life!
2. Christ, the bless-ed One, gives to all Won-der-ful words of Life.
3. Sweet-ly ech-o the gos-pel call, Won-der-ful words of Life!

Let me more of their beau-ty see, Won-der-ful words of Life!
Sin-ner, list to the lov-ing call, Won-der-ful words of Life;
Of-fer par-don and peace to all, Won-der-ful words of Life!

Words of life and beau-ty, Teach me faith and du-ty.
All so free-ly giv-en, Woo-ing us to heav-en.
Je-sus, on-ly Sav-iour, Sanc-ti-fy for-ev-er.

REFRAIN

Beau-ti-ful words, wonderful words, Wonderful words of Life!   Life!

86 Jesus Is All the World to Me

ELIZABETH

Will L. Thompson, 1847 - 1909

Will L. Thompson, 1847 - 1909

1. Je - sus is all the world to me: My Life, my Joy, my All.
2. Je - sus is all the world to me, My Friend in tri - als sore.
3. Je - sus is all the world to me, And true to Him I'll be.
4. Je - sus is all the world to me; I want no bet - ter friend.

He is my Strength from day to day; With - out Him I would fall.
I go to Him for bless - ings, and He gives them o'er and o'er.
Oh, how could I this Friend de - ny When He's so true to me?
I trust Him now; I'll trust Him when Life's fleet - ing days shall end.

When I am sad, to Him I go; No oth - er one can cheer me
He sends the sun - shine and the rain; He sends the har - vest's gold - en
Fol - low - ing Him I know I'm right. He watch - es o'er me day and
Beau - ti - ful life with such a Friend; Beau - ti - ful life that has no

so. When I am sad, He makes me glad. He's my Friend.
grain: Sun - shine and rain, har - vest of grain— He's my Friend.
night. Fol - low - ing Him by day and night, He's my Friend.
end! E - ter - nal life, e - ter - nal joy, He's my Friend!

87 A Child of the King

Harriet E. Buell, 1834-1910

Arr. by John B. Sumner, 1838-1918

1. My Fa - ther is rich in hous - es and lands; He hold - eth the
2. My Fa - ther's own Son, the Sav - iour of men, Once wandered o'er
3. I once was an out - cast stran - ger on earth, A sin - ner by
4. A tent or a cot - tage, why should I care? They're build - ing a

wealth of the world in His hands! Of ru - bies and dia - monds, of
earth as the poor - est of them; But now He is reign - ing for-
choice, an al - ien by birth! But I've been a - dopt - ed; my
pal - ace for me o - ver there! Tho' ex - iled from home, yet

sil - ver and gold, His cof - fers are full— He has rich - es un - told.
ev - er on high, And will give me a home in heav'n by and by.
name's written down. I'm heir to a man - sion, a robe, and a crown!
still I may sing: "All glo - ry to God, I'm a child of the King!"

REFRAIN

I'm a child of the King! A child of the King!

With Je - sus, my Sav - iour, I'm a child of the King!

88 Sunlight, Sunlight

Judson W. Van DeVenter, 1855-1939

Winfield S. Weeden, 1847-1908

1. I wan-dered in the shades of night Till Je-sus came to me,
2. Tho' clouds may gath-er in the sky, And bil-lows 'round me roll,
3. While walk-ing in the light of God, I sweet com-mu-nion find;
4. I cross the wide-ex-tend-ed fields, I jour-ney o'er the plain,
5. Soon I shall see Him as He is, The Light that came to me;

And with the sun-light of His love Bid all my dark-ness flee.
How-ev-er dark the world may be, I've sun-light in my soul.
I press with ho-ly vig-or on, And leave the world be-hind.
And in the sun-light of His love I reap the gold-en grain.
Be-hold the bright-ness of His face Thro'-out e-ter-ni-ty.

REFRAIN

Sun-light, sun-light in my soul to day! Sun-light, sun-light
to-day, yes,

all a-long the way! Since the Sav-iour found me, took a-way my
nar-row way!

sin, I have had the sun-light of His love with-in.
load of sin,

89 Take the Name of Jesus with You

PRECIOUS NAME

Lydia Baxter, 1809 - 1874

William H. Doane, 1832 - 1915

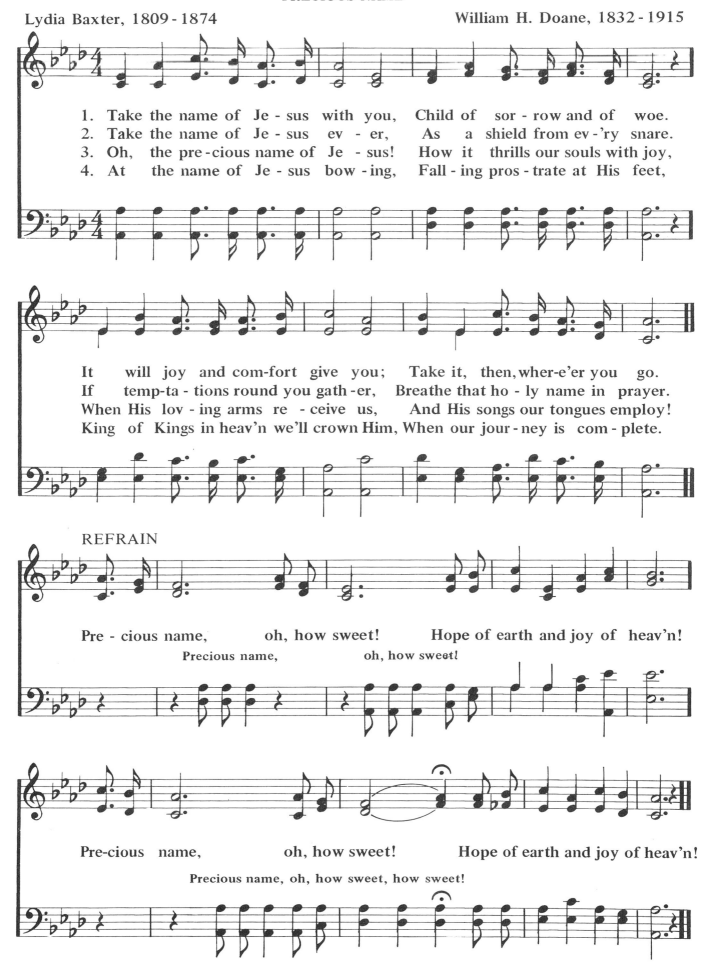

1. Take the name of Je - sus with you, Child of sor - row and of woe.
2. Take the name of Je - sus ev - er, As a shield from ev - 'ry snare.
3. Oh, the pre - cious name of Je - sus! How it thrills our souls with joy,
4. At the name of Je - sus bow - ing, Fall - ing pros - trate at His feet,

It will joy and com - fort give you; Take it, then, wher - e'er you go.
If temp - ta - tions round you gath - er, Breathe that ho - ly name in prayer.
When His lov - ing arms re - ceive us, And His songs our tongues employ!
King of Kings in heav'n we'll crown Him, When our jour - ney is com - plete.

REFRAIN

Pre - cious name, oh, how sweet! Hope of earth and joy of heav'n!
Precious name, oh, how sweet!

Pre - cious name, oh, how sweet! Hope of earth and joy of heav'n!
Precious name, oh, how sweet, how sweet!

90 Living for Jesus

Thomas O. Chisholm, 1866 - 1960

C. Harold Lowden, 1883 -

1. Liv-ing for Je - sus a life that is true, Striv- ing to please Him in
2. Liv-ing for Je - sus, who died in my place, Bear - ing on Cal - v'ry my
3. Liv-ing for Je - sus wher - ev - er I am, Do - ing each du - ty in
4. Liv-ing for Je - sus thro' earth's lit-tle while, My dear - est treas - ure, the

all that I do, Yield-ing al - le-giance, glad-heart-ed and free,
sin and dis - grace— Such love con-strains me to an - swer His call,
His ho - ly name, Will - ing to suf-fer af - flic - tion or loss,
light of His smile, Seek-ing the lost ones He died to re - deem,

REFRAIN

This is the path-way of bless - ing for me.
Fol- low His lead - ing, and give Him my all. O Je-sus, Lord and
Deem-ing each tri - al a part of my cross!
Bring-ing the wea - ry to find rest in Him!

Sav-iour, I give my-self to Thee; For Thou, in Thy a-tone-ment, Didst

give thy-self for me. I own no oth-er Mas-ter; My heart shall be Thy

throne. My life I give, henceforth to live, O Christ, for Thee a - lone.

91 Leaning on the Everlasting Arms

Elisha A. Hoffman, 1839 - 1929   Anthony J. Showalter, 1858 - 1924

1. What a fel - low-ship, what a joy di-vine, Lean-ing on the ev - er - last-ing arms!
2. Oh, how sweet to walk in this pilgrim way, Lean-ing on the ev - er - last-ing arms!
3. What have I to dread, what have I to fear, Lean-ing on the ev - er - last-ing arms?

What a bless-ed - ness, what a peace is mine, Lean-ing on the ev - er - last-ing arms!
Oh, how bright the path grows from day to day, Lean-ing on the ev - er - last-ing arms!
I have bless - ed peace with my Lord so near, Lean-ing on the ev - er - last-ing arms.

REFRAIN

Lean - ing, lean - ing, Safe and se-cure from all a-larms;
Lean - ing on Je - sus, lean - ing on Je - sus,

Lean - ing, lean - ing, Lean - ing on the ev-er-last-ing arms.
Lean - ing on Je - sus, lean - ing on Je - sus,

92 The Lily of the Valley

SALVATIONIST

Charles W. Fry, 1837-1882

English Melody
William S. Hays, 1837-1907

1. I've found a Friend in Je-sus. He's ev-'ry-thing to me. He's the
2. He all my griefs has ta-ken, and all my sor-rows borne. In temp-
3. He'll nev-er, nev-er leave me, nor yet for-sake me here, While I

fair-est of ten thou-sand to my soul. The Lil-y of the Val-ley, in
ta-tion He's my strong and might-y Tow'r. I've all for Him for-sa-ken; I've
live by faith and do His bless-ed will. A wall of fire a-bout me, I've

D.S. Lil-y of the Val-ley, the

Fine

Him a-lone I see All I need to cleanse and make me ful-ly whole.
all my i-dols torn From my heart, and now He keeps me by His pow'r.
noth-ing now to fear. With His man-na He my hun-gry soul shall fill.

Bright and Morning Star. He's the fair-est of ten thou-sand to my soul.

In sor-row He's my Com-fort; in trou-ble He's my Stay.
Tho' all the world for-sake me, and Sa-tan tempt me sore,
Then sweep-ing up to glo-ry, I'll see His bless-ed face,

D.S.

He tells me ev-'ry care on Him to roll. (Hal-le-lu-jah!)
Thro' Je-sus I shall safe-ly reach the goal.
Where riv-ers of de-light shall ev-er roll. He's the

93 Jesus Loves Even Me

GLADNESS

Philip P. Bliss, 1838-1876   Philip P. Bliss, 1838-1876

1. I am so glad that our Fa-ther in heav'n Tells of His love in the
2. Tho' I for-get Him and wan-der a-way, Still He doth love me wher-
3. Oh, if there's on-ly one song I can sing When in His beau-ty I

Book He has giv'n. Won-der-ful things in the Bi-ble I see;
ev-er I stray. Back to His dear, lov-ing arms would I flee
see the great King, This shall my song in e-ter-ni-ty be:

REFRAIN

This is the dear-est, that Je-sus loves me.
When I re-mem-ber that Je-sus loves me. I am so glad that
"Oh, what a won-der that Je-sus loves me!"

Je-sus loves me, Je-sus loves me, Je-sus loves me!

I am so glad that Je-sus loves me, Je-sus loves e-ven me!

94   Sweeter as the Years Go By

Lelia N. Morris, 1862-1929   Lelia N. Morris, 1862-1929

1. Of Je - sus' love that sought me When I was lost in sin; Of wondrous
2. He trod in old Ju - de - a Life's path - way long a - go; The peo - ple
3. 'Twas wondrous love which led Him For us to suf - fer loss—To bear with-

grace that brought me Back to His fold a - gain; Of heights and depths of
thronged a-bout Him, His sav - ing grace to know. He healed the bro - ken-
out a mur - mur The an-guish of the Cross. With saints re - deemed in

mer - cy, Far deep - er than the sea, And high - er than the heav-ens,
heart-ed, And caused the blind to see; And still His great heart yearneth
glo - ry, Let us our voic - es raise, Till heav'n and earth re - ech - o

REFRAIN

My theme shall ev - er be.
In love for e - ven me. Sweet-er as the years go by,_____
With our Re - deem-er's praise. Sweet - er as the years go by,'Tis

Sweet - er as the years go by;_____ Rich - er, full - er, deep - er,
Sweet - er as the years go by;

Copyright 1912. Renewed 1940 by Nazarene Publishing House.

Je - sus' love is sweet - er, Sweet - er as the years go by.

95 Friendship with Jesus

Joe C. Ludgate, 19th Century

Arr. from Stephen Foster, 1826 - 1864

1. A friend of Je - sus! Oh, what bliss That one so vile as I
2. A Friend when other friendships cease, A Friend when oth-ers fail,
3. A Friend when sickness lays me low, A Friend when death draws near,
4. A Friend when life's short race is o'er, A Friend when earth is past,

Should ev - er have a Friend like this To lead me to the sky!
A Friend who gives me joy and peace, A Friend when foes as-sail!
A Friend as thro' the vale I go, A Friend to help and cheer!
A Friend to meet on heav - en's shore, A Friend when home at last!

REFRAIN

Friend - ship with Je - sus! Fel - low - ship di - vine!

Oh, what bless-ed, sweet com-mu - nion! Je - sus is a Friend of mine.

96 I Love to Tell the Story

HANKEY

Katherine Hankey, 1834-1911

William G. Fischer, 1835-1912

1. I love to tell the sto - ry Of un-seen things a - bove, Of Je-sus
2. I love to tell the sto - ry; More won-der-ful it seems Than all the
3. I love to tell the sto - ry; 'Tis pleas-ant to re-peat What seems each
4. I love to tell the sto - ry, For those who know it best Seem hunger-

and His glo - ry, Of Je - sus and His love. I love to tell the sto - ry
gold-en fan-cies Of all our gol-den dreams. I love to tell the sto - ry;
time I tell it More won-der-ful - ly sweet. I love to tell the sto - ry,
ing and thirsting To hear it like the rest. And when in scenes of glo - ry

Be-cause I know 'tis true. It sat-is - fies my long-ings As nothing else can do.
It did so much for me, And that is just the rea - son I tell it now to thee.
For some have never heard The mes-sage of salvation From God's own holy Word.
I sing the new, new song, 'Twill be the old, old sto - ry That I have loved so long.

REFRAIN

I love to tell the sto - ry! 'Twill be my theme in glo - ry

To tell the old, old sto - ry Of Je - sus and His love.

Redeemed

Fanny J. Crosby, 1820 - 1915

William J. Kirkpatrick, 1838 - 1921

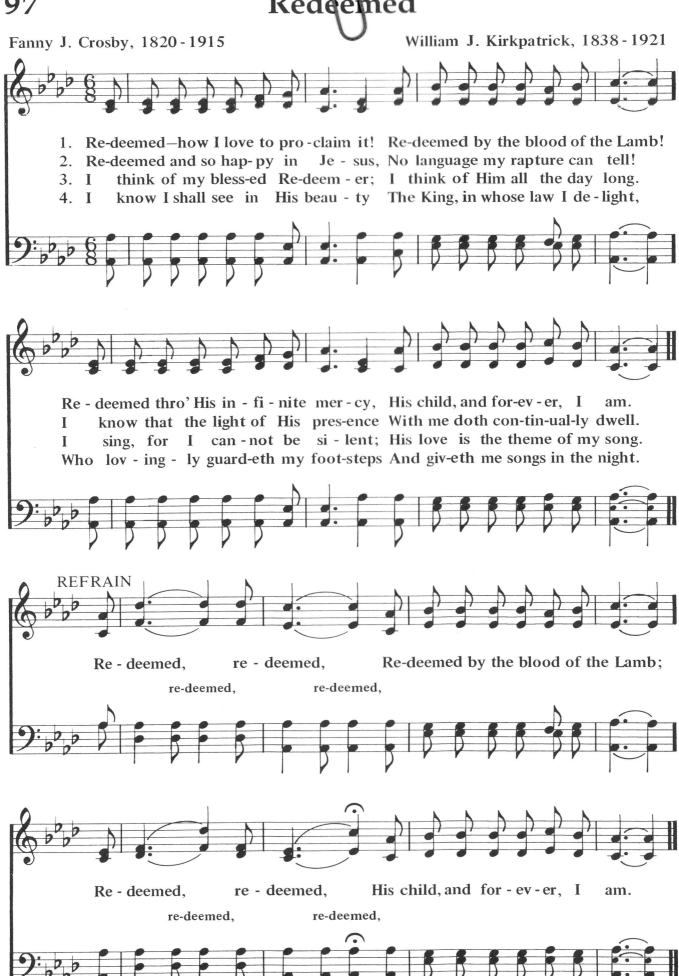

1. Re-deemed—how I love to pro-claim it! Re-deemed by the blood of the Lamb!
2. Re-deemed and so hap-py in Je - sus, No language my rapture can tell!
3. I think of my bless-ed Re-deem - er; I think of Him all the day long.
4. I know I shall see in His beau - ty The King, in whose law I de - light,

Re - deemed thro' His in - fi - nite mer - cy, His child, and for-ev - er, I am.
I know that the light of His pres-ence With me doth con-tin-ual-ly dwell.
I sing, for I can-not be si - lent; His love is the theme of my song.
Who lov - ing - ly guard-eth my foot-steps And giv-eth me songs in the night.

REFRAIN

Re - deemed, re - deemed, Re-deemed by the blood of the Lamb;
re-deemed, re-deemed,

Re - deemed, re - deemed, His child, and for - ev - er, I am.
re-deemed, re-deemed,

98 Since Jesus Came into My Heart

R. H. McDaniel, 20th Century

Charles H. Gabriel, 1856-1932

1. What a won-der-ful change in my life has been wrought Since Je-sus came
2. I have ceased from my wand'ring and go-ing a-stray Since Je-sus came
3. I'm pos-sessed of a hope that is stead-fast and sure, Since Je-sus came
4. There's a light in the val-ley of death now for me, Since Je-sus came
5. I shall go there to dwell in that cit-y I know, Since Je-sus came

in-to my heart! I have light in my soul for which long I had sought,
in-to my heart; And my sins which were man-y are all washed a-way,
in-to my heart; And no dark clouds of doubt now my pathway ob-scure,
in-to my heart; And the gates of the cit-y be-yond I can see,
in-to my heart; And I'm hap-py, so hap-py, as on-ward I go,

REFRAIN

Since Je-sus came in-to my heart. Since Je-sus came in-to my
came in, came

heart, Since Je-sus came in-to my heart, Floods of joy o'er my
in-to my heart, Since Je-sus came in, came in-to my heart,

soul like the sea bil-lows roll, Since Je-sus came in-to my heart.

99 O Happy Day

Philip Doddridge, 1702-1751

Edward F. Rimbault, 1816-1876

1. O hap-py day that fixed my choice On Thee, my Sav-iour and my God!
2. 'Tis done, the great trans-ac-tion's done; I am my Lord's and He is mine.
3. Now rest, my long di-vid-ed heart; Fixed on this bliss-ful cen-ter, rest;

Well may this glow-ing heart re-joice, And tell its rap-tures all a-broad.
He drew me, and I fol-lowed on, Charmed to con-fess the voice di-vine.
Nor ev-er from my Lord de-part, With Him of ev-'ry good pos-sessed.

Fine

Hap-py day, hap-py day, When Je-sus washed my sins a-way!

D.S.

He taught me how to watch and pray, And live re-joic-ing ev-'ry day.

100 The Old Rugged Cross

George Bennard, 1873-1958   George Bennard, 1873-1958

1. On a hill far a-way stood an old rug-ged Cross, The em-blem of
2. Oh, the old rug-ged Cross, so de-spised by the world, Has a won-drous at-
3. In the old rug-ged Cross, stained with Blood so divine, A won-drous
4. To the old rug-ged Cross I will ev-er be true, Its shame and re-

suf-f'ring and shame; And I love that old Cross, where the dear-est and best
trac-tion for me; For the dear Lamb of God left His glo-ry a-bove
beau-ty I see; For 'twas on that old Cross Je-sus suf-fered and died
proach glad-ly bear. Then He'll call me some-day to my home far a-way,

REFRAIN

For a world of lost sin-ners was slain.
To bear it to dark Cal-va-ry. So I'll cher-ish the old rug-ged
To par-don and sanc-ti-fy me.
Where His glo-ry for-ev-er I'll share.
     Cross, the

Cross,_____ Till my tro-phies at last I lay down. I will cling to the
old rug-ged Cross,

old rug-ged Cross,_____ And ex-change it some-day for a crown.
Cross, the old rug-ged Cross,

101 At the Cross

HUDSON

Isaac Watts, 1674 - 1748
Refrain by Ralph E. Hudson, 1843 - 1901

Ralph E. Hudson, 1843 - 1901

1. A - las! and did my Sav - iour bleed, And did my Sov - 'reign
2. Was it for crimes that I have done He groaned up - on the
3. Well might the sun in dark - ness hide, And shut his glo - ries
4. But drops of grief can ne'er re - pay The debt of love I

die? Would He de - vote that sa - cred head For such a worm as I?
tree? A - maz - ing pit - y, grace unknown, And love be - yond de - gree!
in When Christ, the mighty Mak - er, died For man, the creature's, sin.
owe. Here, Lord, I give my - self a - way; 'Tis all that I can do!

REFRAIN

At the Cross, at the Cross, where I first saw the light, And the

bur - den of my heart rolled a - way, rolled a - way. It was there by faith

I re - ceived my sight, And now I am hap - py all the day!

102 When I Survey

HAMBURG

Isaac Watts, 1674-1748

Arr. by Lowell Mason, 1792-1872

1. When I sur-vey the won-drous Cross On which the
2. For-bid it, Lord, that I should boast, Save in the
3. See, from His head, His hands, His feet, Sor-row and
4. Were the whole realm of na-ture mine, That were a

Prince of Glo-ry died, My rich-est gain I
death of Christ, my God. All the vain things that
love flow min-gled down. Did e'er such love and
pres-ent far too small. Love so a-maz-ing,

count but loss, And pour con-tempt on all my pride.
charm me most, I sac-ri-fice them to His blood.
sor-row meet, Or thorns com-pose so rich a crown?
so di-vine, De-mands my soul, my life, my all.

103 'Tis Midnight

OLIVE'S BROW

William B. Tappan, 1794-1849

William B. Bradbury, 1816-1868

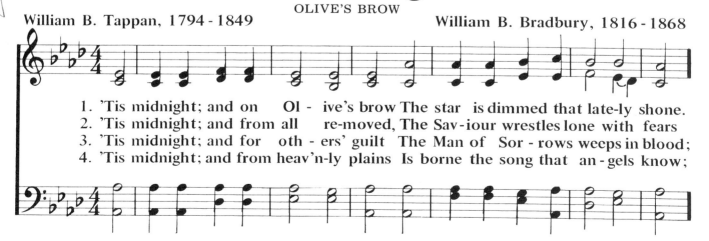

1. 'Tis midnight; and on Ol-ive's brow The star is dimmed that late-ly shone.
2. 'Tis midnight; and from all re-moved, The Sav-iour wrestles lone with fears
3. 'Tis midnight; and for oth-ers' guilt The Man of Sor-rows weeps in blood;
4. 'Tis midnight; and from heav'n-ly plains Is borne the song that an-gels know;

'Tis midnight; in the gar - den now The suff'ring Sav-iour prays a - lone.
E'en that dis - ci - ple whom He loved Heeds not his Master's grief and tears.
Yet He that hath in an - guish knelt Is not for - sak - en by His God.
Un - heard by mor - tals are the strains That sweetly soothe the Saviour's woe.

104 Near the Cross

Fanny J. Crosby, 1820 - 1915   William H. Doane, 1832 - 1915

1. Je - sus, keep me near the Cross. There a pre - cious foun - tain,
2. Near the Cross, a trem - bling soul, Love and mer - cy found me;
3. Near the Cross! O Lamb of God, Bring its scenes be - fore me;
4. Near the Cross I'll watch and wait, Hop - ing, trust - ing ev - er,

'Free to all, a heal - ing stream, Flows from Cal - v'ry's mountain.
There the Bright and Morn - ing Star Sheds its beams a - round me.
Help me walk from day to day With its shad - ows o'er me.
Till I reach the gold - en strand, Just be - yond the riv - er.

REFRAIN

In the Cross, in the Cross Be my glo - ry ev - er,

Till my rap - tured soul shall find Rest be - yond the riv - er.

105 There Is a Fountain

CLEANSING FOUNTAIN

William Cowper, 1731 - 1800

Early American Melody
Arr. from Lowell Mason, 1792 - 1872

1. There is a foun-tain filled with blood Drawn from Im-man-uel's veins;
2. The dy-ing thief re-joiced to see That foun-tain in his day;
3. Dear dy-ing Lamb, Thy pre-cious blood Shall nev-er lose its pow'r
4. E'er since, by faith, I saw the stream Thy flow-ing wounds sup-ply,
5. Then in a no-bler, sweet-er song I'll sing Thy pow'r to save,

And sin-ners, plunged be-neath that flood, Lose all their guilt-y stains:
And there may I, though vile as he, Wash all my sins a-way:
Till all the ran-somed Church of God Be saved, to sin no more:
Re-deem-ing love has been my theme And shall be till I die:
When this poor lisp-ing, stamm'ring tongue Lies si-lent in the grave:

Lose all their guilt-y stains, Lose all their guilt-y stains;
Wash all my sins a-way, Wash all my sins a-way;
Be saved, to sin no more, Be saved, to sin no more;
And shall be till I die, And shall be till I die;
Lies si-lent in the grave, Lies si-lent in the grave;

And sin-ners, plunged be-neath that flood, Lose all their guilt-y stains.
And there may I, though vile as he, Wash all my sins a-way.
Till all the ran-somed Church of God Be saved, to sin no more.
Re-deem-ing love has been my theme And shall be till I die.
When this poor lisp-ing, stamm'ring tongue Lies si-lent in the grave.

106 Beneath the Cross of Jesus

ST. CHRISTOPHER

Elizabeth C. Clephane, 1830 - 1869

Frederick C. Maker, 1844 - 1927

1. Be -neath the cross of Je - sus I fain would take my stand,
2. Up - on the cross of Je - sus Mine eyes at times can see
3. I take, O Cross, thy shad - ow For my a - bid - ing place.

The shad - ow of a might - y rock With - in a wea - ry land;
The ver - y dy - ing form of One Who suf - fered there for me.
I ask no oth - er sun - shine than The sun - shine of His face;

A home with-in the wil - der - ness; A rest up-on the way,
And from my smit- ten heart, with tears, These won - ders I con - fess:
Con - tent to let the world go by, To know no gain nor loss,

From the burn - ing of the noon-tide heat And the bur - den of the day.
The won - der of His glo -rious love, And my un-wor -thi - ness.
My sin - ful self my on - ly shame, My glo - ry all the Cross.

107 A Charge to Keep I Have

BOYLSTON

Charles Wesley, 1707-1788

Lowell Mason, 1792-1872

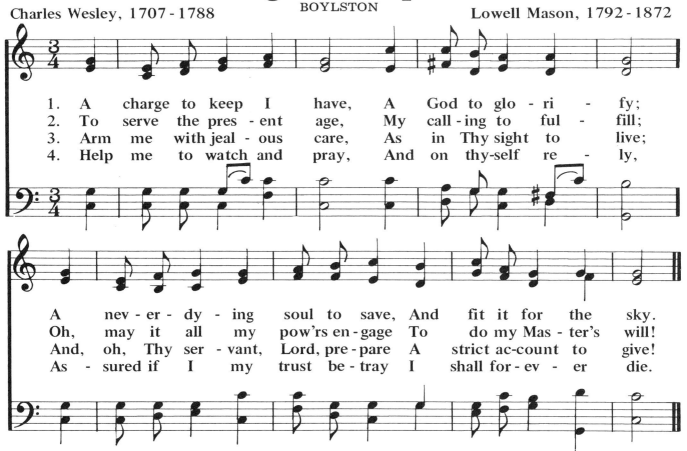

1. A charge to keep I have, A God to glo - ri - fy;
2. To serve the pres - ent age, My call - ing to ful - fill;
3. Arm me with jeal - ous care, As in Thy sight to live;
4. Help me to watch and pray, And on thy - self re - ly,

A nev - er - dy - ing soul to save, And fit it for the sky.
Oh, may it all my pow'rs en - gage To do my Mas - ter's will!
And, oh, Thy ser - vant, Lord, pre - pare A strict ac - count to give!
As - sured if I my trust be - tray I shall for - ev - er die.

108 Must Jesus Bear the Cross Alone?

MAITLAND

Thomas Shepherd, 1665-1739

George N. Allen, 1812-1877

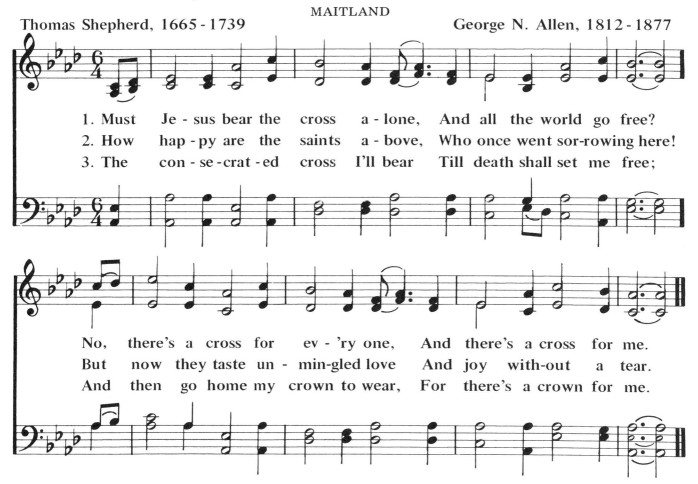

1. Must Je - sus bear the cross a - lone, And all the world go free?
2. How hap - py are the saints a - bove, Who once went sor - rowing here!
3. The con - se - crat - ed cross I'll bear Till death shall set me free;

No, there's a cross for ev - 'ry one, And there's a cross for me.
But now they taste un - min - gled love And joy with - out a tear.
And then go home my crown to wear, For there's a crown for me.

109 The Way of the Cross Leads Home

Jessie Brown Pounds, 1861 - 1921

Charles H. Gabriel, 1856 - 1932

1. I must needs go home by the way of the Cross; There's no oth-er
2. I must needs go on in the Blood-sprin-kled way, The path that the
3. Then I bid fare-well to the way of the world, To walk in it

way but this. I shall ne'er get sight of the Gates of Light
Sav-iour trod, If I ev-er climb to the heights sub-lime,
nev-er-more; For my Lord says, "Come," and I seek my home,

If the way of the Cross I miss.
Where the soul is at home with God.
Where He waits at the o-pen door.

REFRAIN

The way of the Cross leads home. The way of the Cross leads home. It is

leads home.
leads home.

sweet to know, as I on-ward go, The way of the Cross leads home.

110 Christ Arose

Robert Lowry, 1826 - 1899

Robert Lowry, 1826 - 1899

1. Low in the grave He lay— Je - sus, my Sav - iour! Wait- ing the coming day—
2. Vain - ly they watch His bed— Je - sus, my Sav - iour! Vain-ly they seal the dead—
3. Death cannot keep his prey— Je - sus, my Sav - iour! He tore the bars a-way—

REFRAIN *faster*

Je - sus, my Lord! Up from the grave He a - rose, With a
He a-rose,

might-y tri - umph o'er His foes. He a - rose a Vic-tor from the
He a-rose!

dark do - main, And He lives for - ev - er with His saints to reign. He a-

rit.

rose! He a - rose! Hal - le - lu - jah! Christ a - rose!
He a-rose! He a-rose!

111 Christ, the Lord, Is Risen Today

EASTER HYMN

Charles Wesley, 1707 - 1788

From "Lyra Davidica," 1708

1. Christ, the Lord, is risen to - day.
2. Lives a - gain our glo - rious King.
3. Love's re - deem - ing work is done.
4. Soar we now where Christ has led.

Al - le - lu - ia!

Sons of men and an - gels say:
Where, O death, is now thy sting?
Fought the fight, the bat - tle won.
Fol - lowing our ex - alt - ed Head,

Al - le - lu - ia!

Raise your joys and tri - umphs high.
Dy - ing once, He all doth save.
Death in vain for - bids Him rise.
Made like Him, like Him we rise.

Al - le - lu - ia!

Sing, ye heavens, and, earth, re - ply,
Where thy vic - to - ry, O grave?
Christ has o - pened par - a - dise.
Ours the cross, the grave, the skies.

Al - le - lu - ia!

112 Crown Him with Many Crowns

DIADEMATA

Matthew Bridges, 1800-1894, and
Godfrey Thring, 1823-1903

George J. Elvey, 1816-1893

1. Crown Him with man-y crowns, The Lamb up-on His throne.
2. Crown Him the Lord of Love! Be-hold His hands and side—
3. Crown Him the Lord of Life! Who tri-umphed o'er the grave;
4. Crown Him the Lord of Heav'n! One with the Fa-ther known,

Hark! how the heav'n-ly an-them drowns All mu-sic but its own!
Rich wounds, yet vis-i-ble a-bove, In beau-ty glo-ri-fied.
Who rose vic-to-rious to the strife For those He came to save.
One with the Spir-it thro' Him giv'n From yon-der glo-rious throne!

A-wake, my soul, and sing Of Him who died for thee, And
All hail, Re-deem-er, hail! For Thou hast died for me. Thy
His glo-ries now we sing Who died and rose on high, Who
To Thee be end-less praise, For Thou for us hast died. Be

hail Him as Thy match-less King Thro' all e-ter-ni-ty.
praise shall nev-er, nev-er fail Thro'-out e-ter-ni-ty.
died e-ter-nal life to bring, And lives that death may die.
Thou, O Lord, thro' end-less days A-dored and mag-ni-fied.

113 And Can It Be?

SAGINA

Charles Wesley, 1707 - 1788

Thomas Campbell, 1777 - 1844

1. And can it be that I should gain An in - t'rest in the Sav - iour's blood! Died He for me, who caused His pain? For me, who Him to death pur - sued? A - maz-ing love! How can it be That Thou, my God, shouldst die for me?

2. He left His Fa - ther's throne a - bove, So free, so in - fi - nite His grace! Emp-tied him-self of all but love, And bled for Ad - am's help - less race. 'Tis mer-cy all, im - mense and free! For, O my God, it found out me!

3. Long my im - pris - oned spir - it lay, Fast bound in sin and na - ture's night. Thine eyes dif-fused a quick-'ning ray. I woke; the dun - geon flamed with light. My chains fell off; my heart was free. I rose, went forth, and fol - lowed Thee.

REFRAIN

A - maz - ing love! How can it be That Thou, my God, shouldst die for me?

A - maz-ing love!

How can it be That Thou, my God,

114 The Cleansing Wave

KNAPP

Phoebe Palmer Knapp, 1839 - 1908 Phoebe Palmer Knapp, 1839 - 1908

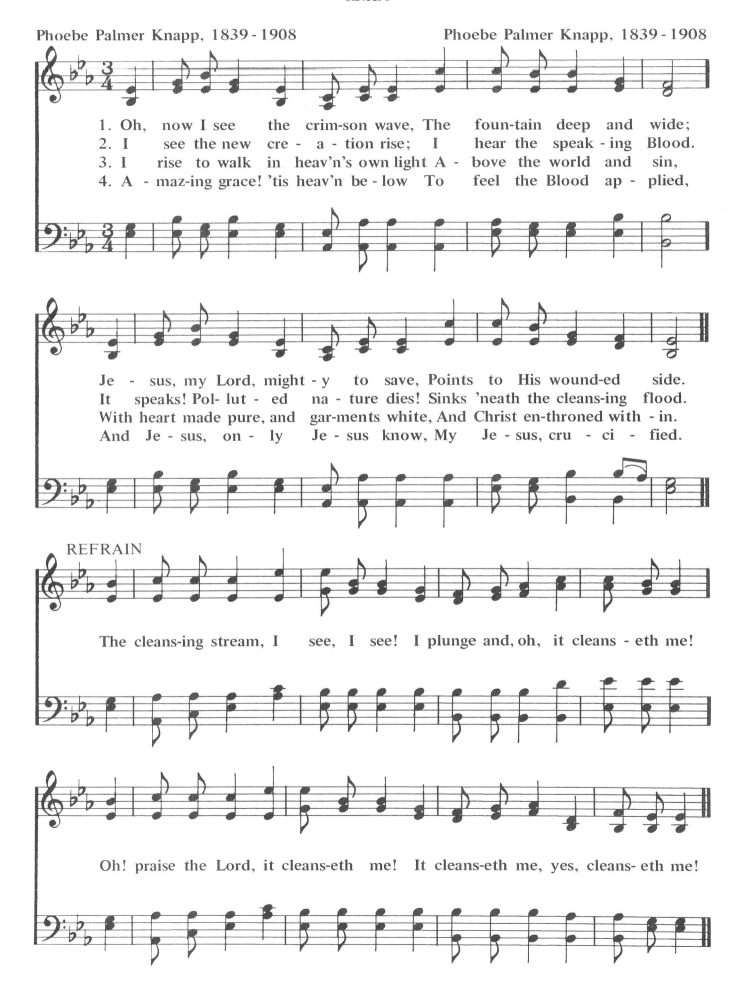

1. Oh, now I see the crim-son wave, The foun-tain deep and wide;
2. I see the new cre - a - tion rise; I hear the speak - ing Blood.
3. I rise to walk in heav'n's own light A - bove the world and sin,
4. A - maz-ing grace! 'tis heav'n be - low To feel the Blood ap - plied,

Je - sus, my Lord, might - y to save, Points to His wound-ed side.
It speaks! Pol- lut - ed na - ture dies! Sinks 'neath the cleans-ing flood.
With heart made pure, and gar-ments white, And Christ en-throned with - in.
And Je - sus, on - ly Je - sus know, My Je - sus, cru - ci - fied.

REFRAIN

The cleans-ing stream, I see, I see! I plunge and, oh, it cleans - eth me!

Oh! praise the Lord, it cleans-eth me! It cleans-eth me, yes, cleans- eth me!

115 Sweet By-and-by

Sanford F. Bennett, 1836-1898

Joseph P. Webster, 1819-1875

1. There's a land that is fair-er than day, And by faith we can see it a - far; For the Fa-ther waits o - ver the way, To pre-pare us a dwell-ing place there.
2. We shall sing on that beau-ti-ful shore The me - lo - di-ous songs of the blest, And our spir - its shall sor - row no more, Not a sigh for the bless-ing of rest.
3. To our boun-ti-ful Fa-ther a-bove We will of - fer our trib-ute of praise, For the glo-ri-ous gift of His love And the bless-ings that hal - low our days.

REFRAIN

In the sweet by-and-by, We shall meet on that beau-ti-ful shore. In the sweet by-and-by, We shall meet on that beau-ti-ful shore.

116 My Saviour First of All

Fanny J. Crosby, 1820-1915

John R. Sweney, 1837-1899

1. When my life-work is end-ed, and I cross the swell-ing tide, When the
2. Oh, the soul-thrill-ing rap-ture when I view His bless-ed face, And the
3. Oh, the dear ones in glo-ry, how they beck-on me to come, And our
4. Thro' the gates to the cit-y in a robe of spot-less white, He will

bright and glorious morning I shall see, I shall know my Re-deem-er when I
lus-ter of His kind-ly beam-ing eye! How my full heart will praise Him for the
part-ing at the riv-er I re-call! To the sweet vales of E-den they will
lead me where no tears will ev-er fall. In the glad song of a-ges I shall

reach the oth-er side, And His smile will be the first to wel-come me.
mer-cy, love, and grace That pre-pare for me a man-sion in the sky!
sing my wel-come home; But I long to meet my Sav-iour first of all.
min-gle with de-light; But I long to meet my Sav-iour first of all.

REFRAIN

I shall know Him. I shall know Him, And redeem'd by His side I shall stand.
I shall know Him.

I shall know Him. I shall know Him By the print of the nails in his hand.
I shall know Him.

117   O That Will Be Glory

Charles H. Gabriel, 1856-1932   Charles H. Gabriel, 1856-1932

1. When all my la - bors and tri - als are o'er, And I am safe on that
2. When, by the gift of His in - fi - nite grace, I am ac - cord - ed in
3. Friends will be there I have loved long a - go; Joy like a riv - er a -

beau - ti - ful shore, Just to be near the dear Lord I a - dore
heav - en a place, Just to be there and to look on His face
round me will flow. Yet, just a smile from my Sav - iour, I know,

rit.   REFRAIN *faster*

Will thro' the a - ges be glo - ry for me. ___ O that will be
O ___ that will

glo - ry for me, Glo - ry for me, glo - ry for me! When by His
be glo - ry for me, Glo - ry for me, glo - ry for me! ___

rit.

grace I shall look on His face, That will be glo - ry, be glo - ry for me.

118 When the Roll Is Called Up Yonder

James M. Black, 1856-1938   James M. Black, 1856-1938

1. When the trum-pet of the Lord shall sound, and time shall be no more, And the
2. On that bright and cloudless morning when the dead in Christ shall rise, And the
3. Let us la-bor for the Mas-ter from the dawn till set-ting sun; Let us

morning breaks, e-ter-nal, bright, and fair; When the saved of earth shall gath-er
glo-ry of His res-ur-rec-tion share; When His cho-sen ones shall gath-er
talk of all His wondrous love and care. Then when all of life is o-ver,

o-ver on the oth-er shore, And the roll is called up yon-der, I'll be there.
to their home be-yond the skies, And the roll is called up yon-der, I'll be there.
and our work on earth is done, And the roll is called up yon-der, I'll be there.

REFRAIN

When the roll_____ is called up yon - der, When the
When the roll is called up yon - der, I'll be there.

roll _____ is called up yon - der, When the roll_____ is called up
When the roll is called up yon-der, I'll be there.   When the roll is called up

yon - der, When the roll is called up yon - der, I'll be there.

119   Saved by Grace
CROSBY

Fanny J. Crosby, 1820 - 1915

George C. Stebbins, 1846 - 1945

1. Some-day the sil - ver cord will break, And I no more as now shall sing.
2. Some-day my earth - ly house will fall; I can-not tell how soon 'twill be.
3. Some-day, when fades the gold - en sun Be-neath the ro - sy - tint - ed west,
4. Some-day—till then I'll watch and wait, My lamp all trimmed and burn-ing bright,

But, oh, the joy when I shall wake With-in the pal - ace of the King!
But this I know— my All in All Has now a place in heav'n for me.
My bless - ed Lord will say, "Well done!" And I shall en - ter in - to rest.
That when my Sav - iour opes the gate, My soul to Him may take its flight.

REFRAIN

And I shall see Him face-to - face, And tell the sto-ry—Saved by grace;
shall see   -to-face,

rit.

And I shall see Him face-to - face And tell the sto-ry—Saved by grace.
shall see   -to-face,

120 When We All Get to Heaven

HEAVEN

Eliza E. Hewitt, 1851 - 1920

Emily D. Wilson, 1865 - 1942

1. Sing the won-drous love of Je - sus; Sing His mer - cy and His grace.
2. While we walk the pil - grim path-way, Clouds will o - ver - spread the sky;
3. Let us then be true and faith-ful, Trust-ing, serv - ing ev - 'ry day.
4. On - ward to the prize be - fore us! Soon His beau - ty we'll be -hold.

In the man-sions, bright and bless - ed, He'll pre -pare for us a place.
But when trav'-ling days are o - ver, Not a shad-ow, not a sigh!
Just one glimpse of Him in glo - ry Will the toils of life re - pay.
Soon the pearl - y gates will o - pen; We shall tread the streets of gold.

for us a place.

REFRAIN

When we all get to heav - en, What a day of re-
When we all What a

joic - ing that will be! When we all see
day of re - joic - ing that will be! When we all

Je - sus, We'll sing and shout the vic - to - ry.
and shout the vic - to - ry.

121 Jesus, I Come

William T. Sleeper, 1819-1904

George C. Stebbins, 1846-1945

1. Out of my bond-age, sor-row, and night, Je-sus, I come; Je-sus, I come.
2. Out of my shame-ful fail-ure and loss, Je-sus, I come; Je-sus, I come.
3. Out of un-rest and ar-ro-gant pride, Je-sus, I come; Je-sus, I come.
4. Out of the fear and dread of the tomb, Je-sus, I come; Je-sus, I come.

In - to Thy free - dom, glad - ness, and light,
In - to the glo - rious gain of Thy cross,
In - to Thy bless - ed will to a - bide,
In - to the joy and light of Thy home,

Je - sus, I come to Thee.

Out of my sick-ness in - to Thy health, Out of my want and in-to Thy wealth,
Out of earth's sorrows in - to Thy balm, Out of life's storms and in-to Thy calm,
Out of my-self to dwell in Thy love, Out of de-spair in-to rap-tures a-bove,
Out of the depths of ru - in un-told, In - to the peace of Thy sheltering fold,

Out of my sin and in - to thy-self,
Out of dis - tress to ju - bi-lant psalm,
Up - ward for aye on wings like a dove,
Ev - er Thy glo - rious face to be-hold,

Je - sus, I come to Thee.

122

Pass Me Not

Fanny J. Crosby, 1820 - 1915

William H. Doane, 1832 - 1915

1. Pass me not, O gen-tle Sav-iour; Hear my hum-ble cry. While on
2. Let me at the throne of mer-cy Find a sweet re-lief; Kneel-ing
3. Trust-ing on-ly in Thy mer-it, Would I seek Thy face. Heal my
4. Thou, the Spring of all my com-fort, More than life to me, Whom have

REFRAIN

oth-ers Thou art call-ing, Do not pass me by.
there in deep con-tri-tion, Help my un-be-lief.
wounded, bro-ken spir-it. Save me by Thy grace.   Sav-iour, Sav-iour,
I on earth be-side Thee? Whom in heav'n but Thee?

Hear my humble cry.   While on oth-ers Thou art call-ing, Do not pass me by.

123

Just as I Am

WOODWORTH

Charlotte Elliott, 1789 - 1871

William B. Bradbury, 1816 - 1868

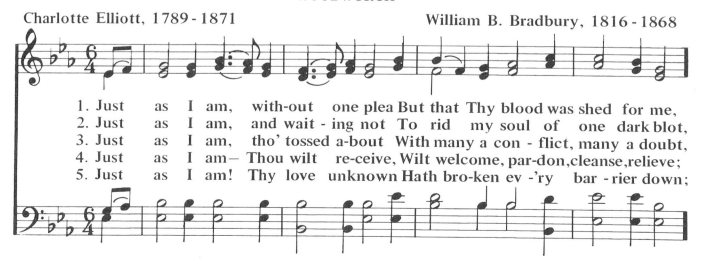

1. Just as I am, with-out one plea But that Thy blood was shed for me,
2. Just as I am, and wait-ing not To rid my soul of one dark blot,
3. Just as I am, tho' tossed a-bout With many a con-flict, many a doubt,
4. Just as I am— Thou wilt re-ceive, Wilt welcome, par-don, cleanse, relieve;
5. Just as I am! Thy love unknown Hath bro-ken ev-'ry bar-rier down;

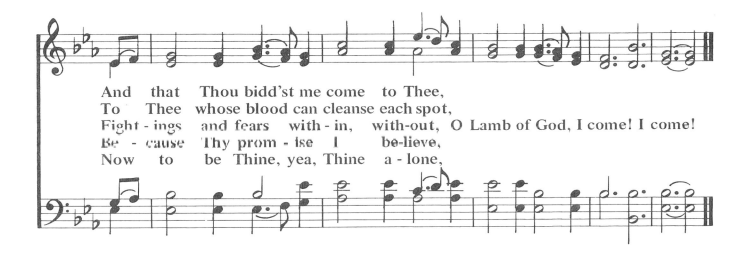

And that Thou bidd'st me come to Thee,
To Thee whose blood can cleanse each spot,
Fight-ings and fears with-in, with-out, O Lamb of God, I come! I come!
Be - cause Thy prom - ise I be-lieve,
Now to be Thine, yea, Thine a - lone,

124   My Faith Looks Up to Thee

OLIVET

Ray Palmer, 1808 - 1887

Lowell Mason, 1792 - 1872

1. My faith looks up to Thee, Thou Lamb of Cal - va-ry,
2. May Thy rich grace im-part Strength to my faint - ing heart,
3. While life's dark maze I tread, And griefs a - round me spread,
4. When ends life's tran - sient dream, When death's cold, sul - len stream

Sav - iour di - vine! Now hear me while I pray; Take all my
My zeal in - spire. As Thou hast died for me, Oh, may my
Be Thou my Guide. Bid dark - ness turn to day; Wipe sor - row's
Shall o'er me roll, Blest Sav - iour, then in love Fear and dis -

guilt a - way. Oh, let me from this day Be whol - ly Thine!
love to Thee Pure, warm, and change-less be, A liv - ing fire!
tears a - way; Nor let me ev - er stray From Thee a - side!
trust re - move. Oh, bear me safe a - bove, A ran - somed soul!

125 His Way with Thee

NUSBAUM

Cyrus S. Nusbaum, 1861 - 1937

Cyrus S. Nusbaum, 1861 - 1937

1. Would you live for Je - sus, and be always pure and good? Would you walk with
2. Would you have Him make you free, and follow at His call? Would you know the
3. Would you in His king-dom find a place of constant rest? Would you prove Him

Him with - in the nar - row road? Would you have Him bear your burden, car - ry
peace that comes by giv - ing all? Would you have Him save you, so that you need
true in prov - i - den-tial test? Would you in His ser-vice la - bor al - ways

REFRAIN

all your load?
nev - er fall? Let Him have His way with thee. His pow'r can make you what you
at your best?

ought to be. His blood can cleanse your heart and make you free. His love can

rit.

fill your soul, and you will see 'Twas best for Him to have His way with thee.

126

Only Trust Him

STOCKTON

John H. Stockton, 1813 - 1877   John H. Stockton, 1813 - 1877

1. Come, ev - 'ry soul by sin op-pressed, There's mer-cy with the Lord;
2. For Je - sus shed His pre - cious blood Rich bless-ings to be - stow.
3. Yes, Je - sus is the Truth, the Way, That leads you in - to rest.

And He will sure-ly give you rest By trust-ing in His Word.
Plunge now in - to the crim - son flood That wash - es white as snow.
Be - lieve in Him with-out de-lay, And you are ful - ly blest.

REFRAIN

On - ly trust Him, on - ly trust Him, On - ly trust Him now;

He will save you, He will save you, He will save you now.

127 Softly and Tenderly

THOMPSON

Will L. Thompson, 1847 - 1909

Will L. Thompson, 1847 - 1909

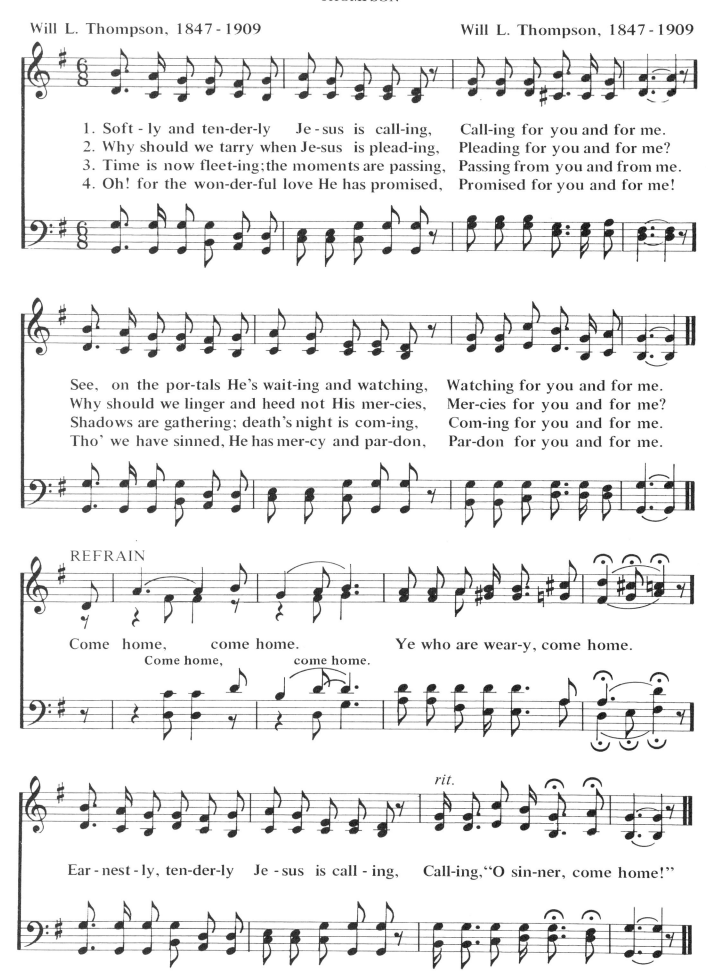

1. Soft - ly and ten-der-ly Je - sus is call-ing, Call-ing for you and for me.
2. Why should we tarry when Je-sus is plead-ing, Pleading for you and for me?
3. Time is now fleet-ing; the moments are passing, Passing from you and from me.
4. Oh! for the won-der-ful love He has promised, Promised for you and for me!

See, on the por-tals He's wait-ing and watching, Watching for you and for me.
Why should we linger and heed not His mer-cies, Mer-cies for you and for me?
Shadows are gathering; death's night is com-ing, Com-ing for you and for me.
Tho' we have sinned, He has mer-cy and par-don, Par-don for you and for me.

REFRAIN

Come home, come home. Ye who are wear-y, come home.

Come home, come home.

Ear - nest - ly, ten-der-ly Je - sus is call - ing, Call-ing, "O sin-ner, come home!"

128 Mine Eyes Have Seen the Glory

BATTLE HYMN

Julia Ward Howe, 1819 - 1910

John William Steffe, 19th Century

1. Mine eyes have seen the glo - ry of the com-ing of the Lord. He is
2. I have seen Him in the watch fires of a hundred circling camps; They have
3. He has sound-ed forth the trumpet that shall nev - er call re-treat; He is
4. In the beau - ty of the lil - ies Christ was born a-cross the sea, With a

tram-pling out the vin - tage where the grapes of wrath are stored; He hath
build-ed Him an al - tar in the eve - ning dews and damps; I can
sift - ing out the hearts of men be - fore His judg - ment seat. Oh, be
glo - ry in His bos-om that trans-fig - ures you and me. As He

loosed the fate - ful light - ning of His ter - ri - ble, swift sword. His truth is
read His righ - teous sen - tence by the dim and flar - ing lamps. His day is
swift, my soul, to an - swer Him! be ju - bi-lant, my feet! Our God is
died to make men ho - ly, let us die to make men free, While God is

REFRAIN

march-ing on. Glo - ry! glo - ry! Hal - le - lu - jah! Glo - ry! glo - ry! Hal-le-

lu - jah! Glo-ry! glo - ry! Hal - le - lu - jah! His truth is march-ing on.

129 The Star-spangled Banner

NATIONAL ANTHEM OF U.S.A.

Francis Scott Key, 1779 - 1843

John Stafford Smith, 1750 - 1836

1. O say, can you see, by the dawn's ear-ly light, What so
2. On the shore dim - ly seen thro' the mists of the deep, Where the
3. O thus be it ev - er when free - men shall stand Be -

proud - ly we hailed at the twi - light's last gleaming? Whose broad
foe's haugh - ty host in dread si - lence re - pos - es, What is
tween their loved homes and the war's des - o - la - tion! Blest with

stripes and bright stars, thro' the per - i - lous fight, O'er the ram-parts we
that which the breeze, o'er the tow - er - ing steep, As it fit - ful - ly
vic - t'ry and peace, may the heav'n-res-cued land Praise the Pow'r that hath

watched, were so gal - lant - ly stream - ing? And the rock - et's red
blows, half con - ceals, half dis - clos - es? Now it catch - es the
made and pre - served us a na - tion! Then con - quer we

glare, the bombs burst-ing in air Gave proof thro' the night that our
gleam of the morn-ing's first beam; In full glo - ry re-flect - ed, now
must, when our cause it is just; And this be our mot-to: "In

flag was still there. O say, does that star-span-gled ban-ner yet
shines on the stream. 'Tis the star-span-gled ban-ner. O long may it
God is our trust!" And the star-span-gled ban-ner in tri-umph shall

wave O'er the land of the free and the home of the brave?
wave O'er the land of the free and the home of the brave!
wave O'er the land of the free and the home of the brave.

130   My Country, 'Tis of Thee

AMERICA

Samuel F. Smith, 1808 - 1895   Henry Carey, 1690 - 1743

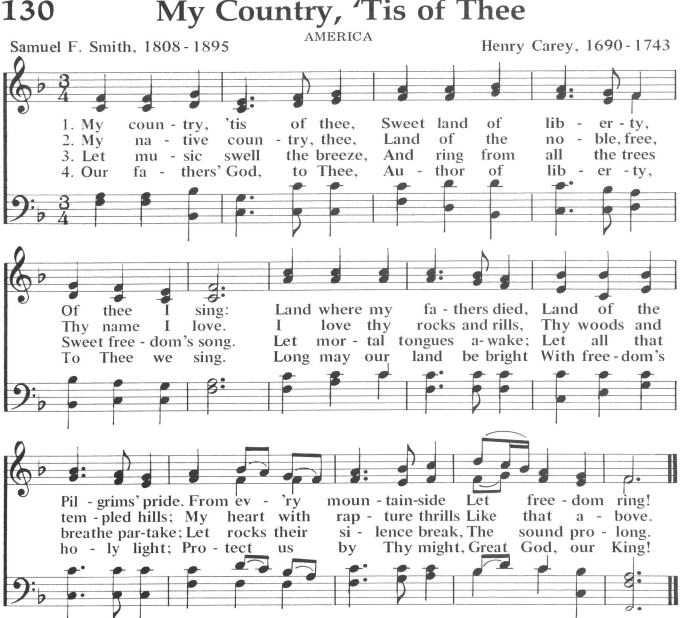

1. My coun-try, 'tis of thee, Sweet land of lib-er-ty,
2. My na-tive coun-try, thee, Land of the no-ble, free,
3. Let mu-sic swell the breeze, And ring from all the trees
4. Our fa-thers' God, to Thee, Au-thor of lib-er-ty,

Of thee I sing: Land where my fa-thers died, Land of the
Thy name I love. I love thy rocks and rills, Thy woods and
Sweet free-dom's song. Let mor-tal tongues a-wake; Let all that
To Thee we sing. Long may our land be bright With free-dom's

Pil-grims' pride. From ev-'ry moun-tain-side Let free-dom ring!
tem-pled hills; My heart with rap-ture thrills Like that a-bove.
breathe par-take; Let rocks their si-lence break, The sound pro-long.
ho-ly light; Pro-tect us by Thy might, Great God, our King!

131 America, the Beautiful

MATERNA

Katherine Lee Bates, 1859-1929

Samuel A. Ward, 1847-1903

1. O beau-ti-ful for spa-cious skies, For am-ber waves of grain,
2. O beau-ti-ful for pil-grim feet, Whose stern, im-pas-sioned stress
3. O beau-ti-ful for he-roes proved In lib-er-at-ing strife,
4. O beau-ti-ful for pa-triot dream That sees be-yond the years

For pur-ple mountain maj-es-ties A-bove the fruit-ed plain!
A thor-ough-fare for free-dom beat A-cross the wil-der-ness!
Who more than self their coun-try loved, And mer-cy more than life!
Thine al-a-bas-ter cit-ies gleam Un-dimmed by hu-man tears!

A-mer-i-ca! A-mer-i-ca! God shed His grace on thee,
A-mer-i-ca! A-mer-i-ca! God mend thine ev-'ry flaw,
A-mer-i-ca! A-mer-i-ca! May God thy gold re-fine
A-mer-i-ca! A-mer-i-ca! God shed His grace on thee,

And crown thy good with broth-er-hood From sea to shin-ing sea!
Con-firm thy soul in self-con-trol, Thy lib-er-ty in law!
Till all suc-cess be no-ble-ness And ev-'ry gain di-vine!
And crown thy good with broth-er-hood From sea to shin-ing sea!

132 O Come, All Ye Faithful

ADESTE FIDELIS

From the Latin, 18th Century
Tr. by Frederick Oakeley, 1802-1880   *From* Wade's "Cantus Diversi," 18th Century

1. O come, all ye faith-ful, joy-ful and tri-um-phant. O
2. Sing, choirs of an-gels, sing in ex-ul-ta-tion. O
3. Yea, Lord, we greet Thee, born this hap-py morn-ing. O

come ye, O come ye to Beth-le-hem. Come and be-hold Him,
sing, all ye bright hosts of heav'n a-bove. Glo-ry to God, all
Je-sus, to Thee be all glo-ry giv'n: Word of the Fa-ther,

REFRAIN

born the King of an-gels.
glo-ry in the high-est! O come, let us a-dore Him! O
now in flesh ap-pear-ing.

come! _____

come, let us a-dore Him! O come, let us a-dore Him, Christ the Lord!

133 Angels, from the Realms of Glory

REGENT SQUARE

James Montgomery, 1771 - 1854

Henry Smart, 1813 - 1879

1. An - gels, from the realms of glo - ry, Wing your flight o'er
2. Shep-herds, in the field a - bid - ing, Watch - ing o'er your
3. Sa - ges, leave your con - tem-pla - tions; Bright - er vi - sions
4. Saints be - fore the al - tar bend - ing, Watch - ing long in

all the earth. Ye who sang cre - a - tion's sto - ry,
flocks by night, God with man is now re - sid - ing;
beam a - far. Seek the great De - sire of Na - tions;
hope and fear, Sud - den - ly the Lord, de - scend-ing,

REFRAIN

Now pro - claim Mes - si - ah's birth.
Yon - der shines the In - fant Light.
Ye have seen His na - tal star.   Come and wor - ship.
In His tem - ple shall ap - pear.

Come and wor - ship. Wor - ship Christ, the new - born King.

134 Joy to the World

ANTIOCH

Isaac Watts, 1674-1748

Arr. from George F. Handel, 1685-1759

1. Joy to the world! the Lord is come; Let earth re-
2. Joy to the world! the Sav - iour reigns; Let men their
3. No more let sin and sor - row grow, Nor thorns in-
4. He rules the world with truth and grace, And makes the

ceive her King. Let ev - 'ry heart pre - pare Him room,
songs em - ploy; While fields and floods, rocks, hills, and plains
fest the ground. He comes to make His bless - ings flow
na - tions prove The glo - ries of His righ - teous - ness,

And heaven and na - ture sing, And heaven and na - ture
Re - peat the sound - ing joy, Re - peat the sound - ing
Far as the curse is found, Far as the curse is
And won - ders of His love, And won - ders of His

(1) And heaven and na - ture sing.

And

sing, And heav - en, and heav - en and na - ture sing.
joy, Re - peat, re - peat the sound-ing joy.
found, Far as, far as the curse is found.
love, And won - ders, won - ders of His love.

heaven and na - ture sing,

135 While Shepherds Watched Their Flocks

CHRISTMAS

Nahum Tate, 1652 - 1715

Arr. from George F. Handel, 1685 - 1759

1. While shep-herds watched their flocks by night, All seat - ed on the ground, The an - gel of the Lord came down, And glo - ry shone a - round, And glo - ry shone a - round.
2. "Fear not," said he, for might-y dread Had seized their trou - bled mind. "Glad tid - ings of great joy I bring To you and all man - kind, To you and all man - kind.
3. "To you, in Da - vid's town, this day Is born, of Da - vid's line, The Sav - iour, who is Christ the Lord; And this shall be the sign, And this shall be the sign:
4. "The heav'n - ly Babe you there shall find To hu - man view dis - played, All mean - ly wrapped in swath-ing bands, And in a man - ger laid, And in a man - ger laid."
5. "All glo - ry be to God on high, And to the earth be peace. Good - will hence-forth from heav'n to men Be - gin and nev - er cease, Be - gin and nev - er cease!"

136 Away in a Manger

MUELLER

Stanzas 1 and 2 anonymous
Stanza 3, John T. McFarland, 1851 - 1913

John R. Murray, 1841 - 1905

1. A - way in a man - ger, No crib for a bed, The lit - tle Lord
2. The cat - tle are low - ing; The poor Ba - by wakes, But lit - tle Lord
3. Be near me, Lord Je - sus; I ask Thee to stay Close by me for-

Stille Nacht! Heilige Nacht!

Text von Joseph Mohr - 1816

Melodie von Fr. Xav. Gruber - 1818

This is taken from the 1855 Franz Xaver Gruber manuscript for soprano, alto, choir and organ. Gruber created this arrangement while serving as choirmaster in Hallein, Austria. The original text was written in 1816 by Rev. Joseph Mohr in Mariapfarr, Austria and the melody was added by Gruber in 1818 in Arnsdorf. The first performance was at Midnight Mass (1818) in Oberndorf.
The six original verses, can be seen on the Internet at http://ingeb.org/Lieder/stillena.html
Cyber-sheet music by frank_petersohn@sunshine.net

Der Notensatz stammt aus einer Fassung von Franz Xaver Gruber in 1855, für Sopran-, Altostimme, Chor und Orgel. Gruber zeichnete diesen Satz während er Chorleiter in Hallein, Österreich war. Der Urtext stammt von Pfarrer Joseph Mohr (1816) in Mariapfarr, Österreich. Die Vertonung von Gruber folgte 1818 in Arnsdorf. Die Uraufführung war bei der Mitternachtsmesse (1818) in Oberndorf. Die sechs Verse des Urtexts sind im Internet bei http://ingeb.org/Lieder/stillena.html zu finden.
Netznoten bei frank_petersohn@sunshine.net

Page 2 - 1855 arrangement by Franz Gruber

Je - sus Laid down His sweet head. The stars in the sky— Looked
Je - sus, No cry - ing He makes. I love Thee, Lord Je - sus! Look
ev - er, And love me, I pray. Bless all the dear chil-dren In

down where He lay, The lit - tle Lord Je - sus, A - sleep on the hay.
down from the sky, And stay by my cra - dle To watch lul - la - by.
Thy ten - der care, And take us to heav-en, To live with Thee there.

137

Silent Night!

STILLE NACHT

Joseph Mohr, 1792 - 1848

Franz Grüber, 1787 - 1863

1. Si - lent night! Ho - ly night! All is calm, all is bright
2. Si - lent night! Ho - ly night! Shep-herds quake at the sight!
3. Si - lent night! Ho - ly night! Son of God, love's pure light

Round yon vir - gin moth-er and Child. Ho - ly In-fant, so ten - der and mild,
Glo - ries stream from heav-en a - far; Heav'n-ly hosts sing, Al - le - lu - ia!
Ra - diant beams from Thy ho-ly face, With the dawn of re - deem - ing grace,

Sleep in heav - en-ly peace, Sleep in heav - en-ly peace.
Christ, the Sav - iour, is born! Christ, the Sav - iour, is born!
Je - sus, Lord, at Thy birth; Je - sus, Lord, at Thy birth.

138 O Little Town of Bethlehem

ST. LOUIS

Phillips Brooks, 1835 - 1893

Lewis H. Redner, 1831 - 1908

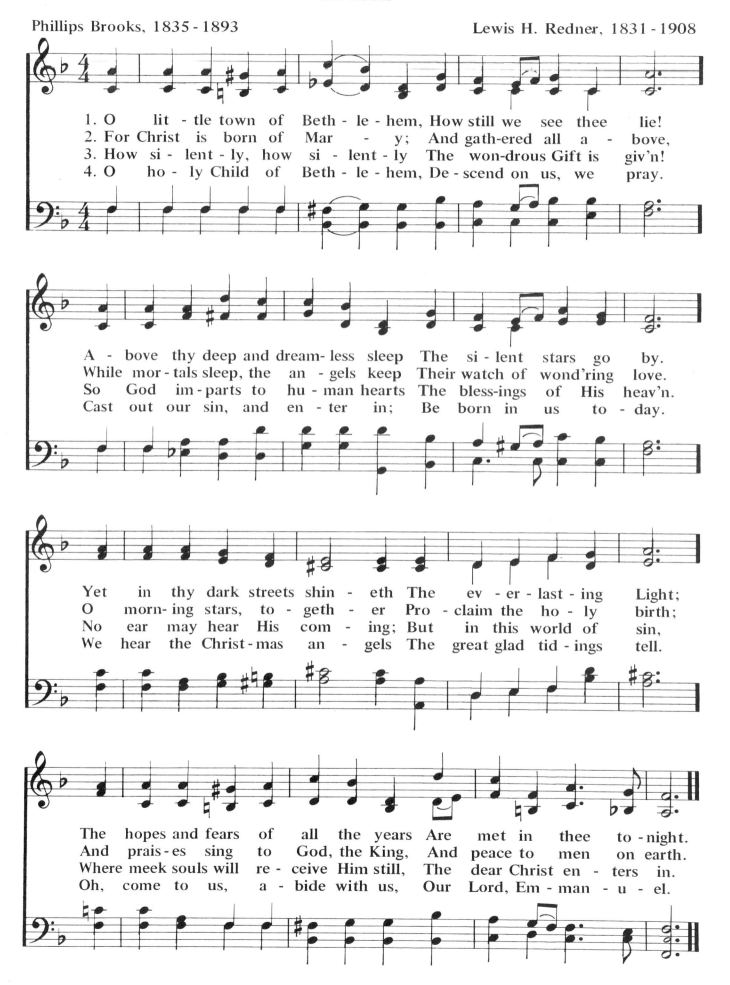

1. O lit - tle town of Beth - le - hem, How still we see thee lie!
2. For Christ is born of Mar - y; And gath-ered all a - bove,
3. How si - lent - ly, how si - lent - ly The won-drous Gift is giv'n!
4. O ho - ly Child of Beth - le - hem, De - scend on us, we pray.

A - bove thy deep and dream-less sleep The si - lent stars go by.
While mor - tals sleep, the an - gels keep Their watch of wond'ring love.
So God im - parts to hu - man hearts The bless-ings of His heav'n.
Cast out our sin, and en - ter in; Be born in us to - day.

Yet in thy dark streets shin - eth The ev - er - last - ing Light;
O morn - ing stars, to - geth - er Pro - claim the ho - ly birth;
No ear may hear His com - ing; But in this world of sin,
We hear the Christ - mas an - gels The great glad tid - ings tell.

The hopes and fears of all the years Are met in thee to - night.
And prais - es sing to God, the King, And peace to men on earth.
Where meek souls will re - ceive Him still, The dear Christ en - ters in.
Oh, come to us, a - bide with us, Our Lord, Em - man - u - el.

139   It Came upon the Midnight Clear

CAROL

Edmund H. Sears, 1810-1876

Richard S. Willis, 1819-1900

1. It came up-on the mid-night clear, That glo-rious song of old,
2. Still thro' the clo-ven skies they come, With peace-ful wings un-furled,
3. And ye, be-neath life's crushing load, Whose forms are bend-ing low,
4. For, lo, the days are hast'n-ing on, By proph-et bards fore-told,

From an-gels bend-ing near the earth To touch their harps of gold.
And still their heav'n-ly mu-sic floats O'er all the wea-ry world.
Who toil a-long the climb-ing way With pain-ful step and slow,
When with the ev-er cir-cling years Comes round the age of gold;

"Peace on the earth, good-will to men, From heav'n's all-gra-cious King."
A-bove its sad and low-ly plains They bend on hov'ring wing,
Look up! For glad and gold-en hours Come swift-ly on the wing.
When peace shall o-ver all the earth Its an-cient splen-dors fling,

The world in sol-emn still-ness lay To hear the an-gels sing.
And ev-er o'er its ba-bel sounds The bless-ed an-gels sing.
Oh, rest be-side the wea-ry road And hear the an-gels sing.
And the whole world give back the song Which now the an-gels sing.

140 Hark! the Herald Angels Sing

MENDELSSOHN

Charles Wesley, 1707-1788
Alt. by George Whitefield, 1714-1770

Felix Mendelssohn, 1809-1847
Adapt. by William H. Cummings, 1831-1915

1. Hark! the her - ald an - gels sing: "Glo - ry to the new-born King!
2. Christ, by high - est heav'n a - dored; Christ, the ev - er - last - ing Lord!
3. Hail, the heav'n-born Prince of Peace! Hail, the Sun of Righ-teous-ness!

Peace on earth, and mer - cy mild; God and sin - ners rec - on-ciled."
Long de-sired, be - hold Him come, Find-ing here His hum-ble home.
Light and life to all He brings, Ris'n with heal - ing in His wings.

Joy - ful, all ye na - tions, rise; Join the tri - umph of the skies;
Veiled in flesh the God-head see; Hail th'in-car - nate De - i - ty!
Let us then with an - gels sing: "Glo - ry to the new-born King!

With th'an-gel - ic hosts pro - claim, "Christ is born in Beth - le - hem."
Pleased as man with men to dwell, Je - sus, our Im-man-u - el!
Peace on earth, and mer - cy mild; God and sin - ners rec - on -ciled."

REFRAIN

Hark! the her-ald an-gels sing, "Glo-ry to the new-born King."

141   There's a Song in the Air

CHRISTMAS SONG

Josiah G. Holland, 1819-1881   Karl P. Harrington, 1861-1953

1. There's a song in the air! There's a star in the sky! There's a moth-er's deep
2. There's a tu-mult of joy O'er the won-der-ful birth, For a Vir-gin's sweet
3. In the light of that star Lie the a-ges impearled; And that song from a-
4. We re-joice in the light, And we ech-o the song That comes down thro' the

prayer And a ba-by's low cry! And the star rains its fire while the
boy Is the Lord of the earth. Ay! the star rains its fire while the
far Has swept o-ver the world. Ev-'ry hearth is a-flame, and the
night From the heav-en-ly throng. Ay! we shout to the love-ly e-

beau-ti-ful sing, For the man-ger of Beth-le-hem cra-dles a King!
beau-ti-ful sing, For the man-ger of Beth-le-hem cra-dles a King!
beau-ti-ful sing In the homes of the na-tions that Je-sus is King!
van-gel they bring, And we greet in His cra-dle our Sav-iour and King!

142　God Rest You Merry, Gentlemen

English Carol, 18th Century　　　　　　　　　　　　　　　Traditional

1. God rest you mer-ry, gen-tle-men; Let noth-ing you dis-may. Re-
2. From God, our Heav'n-ly Fa-ther, A bless-ed an-gel came; And
3. "Fear not, then," said the an-gel; "Let noth-ing you af-fright. This
4. The shep-herds at those tid-ings Re-joic-ed much in mind, And
5. And when they came to Beth-le-hem, Where our dear Sav-iour lay, They

mem-ber Christ, our Sav-iour, Was born on Christ-mas Day, To save us
un-to cer-tain shep-herds Bro't tid-ings of the same: How that in
day is born a Sav-iour Of a pure vir-gin bright, To free all
left their flocks a-feed-ing, In tem-pest, storms, and wind; And went to
found Him in a man-ger, Where ox-en feed on hay. His moth-er,

REFRAIN

all from Sa-tan's pow'r When we were gone a-stray.
Beth-le-hem was born The Son of God by name.
those who trust in Him From Sa-tan's pow'r and might." O　tid-ings of
Beth-le-hem straight-way The Son of God to find.
Mar-y, kneel-ing down, Un-to the Lord did pray.

com-fort and joy, com-fort and joy! O　tid-ings　of com-fort and joy!

143   # The First Noel

English Carol, 17th Century   Traditional Melody

THE GOLDEN HYMNBOOK